PREFACE

The first scientific paper putting a name to bulimia nervosa appeared only twelve years ago (Russell, 1979). However, this disorder was already familiar to a large proportion of the general population. Bulimia and anorexia nervosa affect more than 1 in 200 people in North America and Western Europe causing the sufferers extreme distress, pain and unhappiness as well as being potentially fatal. In England reliable and replicated studies have shown that as many as 2% of women suffer from bulimia nervosa (Cooper et al., 1987) and perhaps 1 in 500 young women suffer from anorexia nervosa (Crisp et al., 1976).

A decade later much more is known by professionals about the clinical features of eating disorders, their long term effects and which groups are most at risk. Although a variety of efficient and effective treatments have been developed there are very few specialist treatment centres for eating disorders. There remain important research questions particularly mechanisms of prevention, although little funding is available to address these research areas. How can this be ? Is it because the majority of those people affected are women ? If a disorder affected 1 in 100 men would more time and energy be spent to eradicate it ?

This book originates in a meeting of the European Council on Eating Disorders held in Ulm, Germany in 1990 when 70 women and men from 12 European countries considered the relevance of gender to eating disorders. This volume is compiled as part of that attempt to understand WHY WOMEN suffer more than men from anorexia and bulimia nervosa and to explore whether women therapists offer something more than their male colleagues to women sufferers.

It was thought that to explore these issues we must look first at the psychological, behavioural, cultural, sexual and political factors which may contribute to the gender specificity of eating disorders. Colleagues who work in ten eating disorders treatment settings in six countries have contributed chapters adressing these issues. We do not claim to produce any final answers to WHY WOMEN ? but we hope to at least further the questioning.

Bridget Dolan
Inez Gitzinger

European Council on Eating Disorders

ACKNOWLEDGEMENTS

We are grateful for the support and encouragement of Professor J. Hubert Lacey, St. George's Medical School, London and Professor Horst Kächele, Forschungstelle für Psychotherapie, Stuttgart.

Immeasurable thanks also go to our friends Chris, Sara, Rose and Annie for being around to help when ever needed.

THE EUROPEAN COUNCIL ON EATING DISORDERS

The European Council on Eating Disorders (ECED) is an informal network of people from throughout Europe who work with eating disorders sufferers in a variety of contexts. We come from a range of settings and professions, involved in therapeutic, academic and research work in both statutory and voluntary sectors.

The principal aim of the ECED is to develop links between workers throughout Europe. We hope by this to share ideas, to further discussion, and to collaborate in work related to all aspects of eating disorders so that treatment and research knowledge is improved.

More information on the ECED can be obtained from Professor Hubert Lacey or Dr. Bridget Dolan at St. George's Medical School, London.

The European Council on Eating Disorders is supported by:

Charter Nightingale Hospital
11-19 Lisson Grove
London NW1 6SH

CONTENTS

WHY WOMEN ? GENDER ISSUES AND EATING DISORDERS

Bridget Dolan

Eating disorders are unique amongst Western psychiatric syndromes in that they offer a plausible sociocultural model of causation. Anorexia nervosa and bulimia are the only psychological disorders which are specific to Western culture and the only ones so specific to women (Dolan 1991).

The majority of writing on anorexia and bulimia nervosa stems from clinical mental health care professions and addresses women as "eating disordered patients" but we should not forget that up to 20% of 'normal' women binge eat once a month, 90% have been on slimming diets and 10% have used vomiting and laxative abuse as a method of dieting at some time (Cooper et al., 1984; Nylander, 1971). In fact disordered eating behaviour and attitudes are so common that as a women you are abnormal if you do not follow diets and worry about your weight. Concerns about the body and self-image are intricately woven into being a woman (Dawson 1990), although we know that the majority of those who resort to dieting will fail (Gilbert 1989).

A popular opinion of anorexia nervosa and bulimia nervosa is that they are "slimmer's diseases" - a vain woman's attempt to be beautiful - with such a view propagated by the media it is not surprising that many non-sufferers are intolerant of their friend's or daughter's lack of ability to stop their disordered eating pattern. This simplistic and incorrect interpretation of eating disorders does not give sufficient credence to the socio-cultural, psychological and political pressures in which women are caught. To understand how eating disorders develop one must consider a range of factors, socio-cultural, familial and individual, which may make a specific person vulnerable to the development and maintenance of eating problems.

Genetically inherited factors give an individual a predetermined shape and a natural body weight. But biological features in isolation would not predispose a woman to an eating disorder. Combine a genetic predisposition, such as being overweight, with the Western socio-cultural pressure on women to feel "abnormal" if fat and we begin to see how the cultural meaning of a biological state may push a woman to manipulate her weight and fight against her biology.

Various common familial factors have been described in women who develop eating problems. Higher parental age, parental marital problems, psychological problems in individual parents such as alcoholic fathers and depressed mothers are often reported. Women with bulimia report repressive sexual attitudes in their families, inability to communicate with their parents, not being understood by their parents (Kog and Vandereycken, 1985; Dolan et al., 1990). In this volume Karin Bell highlights aspects of the mother-daughter relationship which can contribute to the development of bulimia.

The symbolic meanings of bulimia and food for women, both as individuals and as family members have already been well described (Chernin, 1986; Edwards 1987). Eating is a biological necessity, but included amongst its symbolic function, are sexuality, social status, nurturance and care (Greenaway, 1990; Lawrence, 1987). In childhood, physical and emotional care are embodied in being fed by another person, usually a woman. Abuse of food can be seen to symbolise dissatisfaction with this nurturance and, when the abuse is either the restriction of anorexia nervosa or the over-eating in bulimia and obesity, the communication can be very powerful. Refusal of food from the parents can indicate the child's rejection of the parent's overintrusive need to care for them; overeating, or comfort eating, can be a substitute for the care and attention which a person may feel she needs but which is either not available, or is refused. The bulimic woman experiences emotional disturbance but may have no way to express her distress verbally. Instead, the emotional turmoil is translated into the behavioural symptoms of binge eating and vomiting. However, food abuse itself leads to distressing feelings of guilt, shame and disgust, thereby setting up a vicious cycle of negative emotions.

Binge eating usually begins in the mid teenage years, with the onset of vomiting a year or so later. Around this time women are making the transition from child to adult, they are beginning to form their first sexual relationships and the socio-culturally determined valuation of female body shape acquires a personal relevance. A woman from a disordered family who has been using food as a comforter is now faced with a dilemma. Food had been her source of emotional support but now the weight and body shape that result from overeating are contrary to prevailing socio-cultural ideals. A major conflict now exists which can apparently only be resolved by eating excessively but using some measure to prevent weight gain - the resolution is bulimia or anorexia nervosa.

Although one can summarise familial contribution to eating disorders in this way, it is clear that the diversity of the family experiences of women is in great contrast to the uniformity of the age of onset of eating problems (in adolescence and early adulthood) and the remarkable preponderance of female over male sufferers. Any attempt to explain eating disorders should begin with these striking regularities. People with familial stressors can develop a range of different psychological problems. So we need to ask why does a particular person develop an eating problem rather than any other. And we must remember that the 'person' we are talking about is a woman.

Josine Arondeus and Winny Weeda-Mannak, in their paper, outline the conflicts and specific cultural pressures upon women, which influence the development of eating disorders. Concepts of feminine beauty conflict with the modern idea of thinness as a symbol of social and sexual freedom to produce contradictory role definitions for women.

In many societies fatness has been valued over slimness, at least for women. Why has Western society reversed this trend ? One connection is that between fatness and fertility. Fatness can mean ability to nurture, to have children. In some East Africa and Central African countries "fattening sheds" are used where girls at the time of puberty are overfed and have their bodies displayed in a ceremony to signify their reproductive and economic status. It is difficult to conceive of a society which did not have views upon desirable body shape and size, but the question is who controls these views ? Is the Western avoidance of fatness a statement by some women that we do not want to be valued only for our ability to reproduce ? Are we objecting to our bodies being used to signify that someone else is strong and rich enough to feed us ? Are we trying to escape the judgment that a woman's shape dictates her reproductive function which in turn dictates her position and value in society ? Is it a coincidence that the "thinness ideal" developed in parallel with the emancipation of women in the West ? The more women aspire to equality of social status the more society despises the female body with its natural fat deposits, curves and roundness. We are asked to deny our womanhood and our adult status as a sexual, fertile adult, to hate our fat and curves, and to exchange it for an ideal which is similar to the shape of a pre-pubertal child, or a man. Are women exchanging the bondage of one body shape for the enslavement of another ?

A particular difficulty for women and men researchers in this area is the extent to which their own social, personal and political positions influence the generation of research questions. Of neccessity this volume represents a highly selective sample of views and issues within the current field of eating disorders work. Give the plethora of recent publications and interest in sexual abuse it is almost inevitable that connections between abusive sexual experiences and eating disorders are investigated. Incidence of sexual victimisation of children and adults is increasing and we know that female children are at three times greater risk than boys of sexual victimisation (Finkelhor, 1979). The paper by Rachel Calam and Peter Slade highlights how we are only just beginning to understand the importance of adverse sexual experiences for women and whether certain events are specific to the development of eating disorders. Dealing with sexual issues and conflicts is an essential part of therapy in eating disorders. Ellie van Vreckem and Walter Vandereycken describe a therapeutic model devised in Belgium in which women with eating disorders share their experiences of sexual trauma and discuss sexual issues together within a special group programme.

An important aspect of helping women overcome their eating problems, which is given space in this volume, is sharing experiences with other women. This can be within formal group therapy programmes (as described in Belgium), in the community self-help group (as described by Jennifer Munro and Malcolm Laing) or perhaps in individual therapy with a woman therapist. It is a continuing debate whether only women therapists should have exclusive involvement in women's problems. Rose Stockwell considers the gender of the therapist and asks what might contribute to the preferability of women for treating women with eating disorders. Whilst Werner Köpp puts forward some of the arguments for why men can also be successful therapists. Although the focus in this book is on women it should not be forgotten that a minority of men also suffer from eating disorders. Pat Hartley describes how the inclusion of men in community self-help groups (as sufferers, relatives or friends) can enrich the experience of the women in the group whilst for male patients, relatives and clinicians the predominantly female group provides a forum to increase their own understanding of women's experiences.

Any attempt to understand the gender imbalance of eating disorders needs to include men's experiences. Rachel Bryant-Waugh notes how in young anorectics the male-female ratio is much higher than that found in in adolescents and adults. She contends that the role of gender is less central to the development of eating disorders in children than in older age groups. Perhaps we should ask what happens in the continuing socialisation of women which swings the balance so far to the extreme ?

The title of this book is WHY WOMEN ?, it intends to open up more questions than it can answer. Many points made will be theoretical and contentious, all have arguments for and against them. However what has been missing in the clinical literature is not just the answers, but the awareness of how one should form the questions and what those questions are. Edwards (1987) has emphasised how no-one should attempt to understand the psychology of eating problems without considering the wider social context. To do so "would be to fall into the trap which ensnares so many 'neurotic' women: to locate the source of all their problems within themselves, and thus seek exclusively intrapersonal change". Eating disorders have previously been presented as a disorder of women, but perhaps we could ask if they are actually a disorder of our culture ?

REFERENCES

Chernin K. (1986) *The hungry self: Women, eating and identity* London, Virago Press Ltd.

Cooper P., Charnock D. & Taylor M. (1987) The prevalence of bulimia nervosa: A replication study. *British Journal of Psychiatry, 151; 684-686.*

Crisp A., Palmer R. & Kalucy R. (1976) How common is anorexia nervosa ? A prevalence study. *British Journal of Psychiatry, 128, 549-554*

Dawson J. (1990) *How do I look ?* London, Virago Press Ltd.

Dolan B., Lieberman S., Lacey J.H. & Evans C. (1990) Family features associated with normal body weight bulimia. *International Journal of Eating Disorders Vol 9(6); 638-647*

Dolan B. (1991) Cross cultural aspects of anorexia nervosa and bulimia nervosa: A review. *International Journal of Eating Disorders, Vol 10(1); 67-69*

Edwards G (1987) Anorexia and the family - in Lawrence M (op. cit)

Finkelhor D (1979) *Sexually victimised children.* Glencoe, USA; Free Press.

Greenaway P (1990) *The cook, the thief, his wife and her lover.* London, Palace Pictures.

Gilbert S. (1989) *Tomorrow I'll be slim: The psychology of dieting.* London, Routledge

Kog E. & Vandereycken W. (1985) Family characteristics of anorexia nervosa and bulimia: A review of the reserach literature *Clinical Psychology Review 5; 159-180*

Lawrence M. (ed) *Fed up and hungry: Women, opression and food* London, Women's Press Ltd.

Nylander I. (1971) The feeling of being fat and dieting in a school population *Acta Socio-Medica Scandanavica, 1; 17-26*

Russell G. (1979) Bulimia nervosa: an ominous variant of anorexia nervosa *Psychological Medicine, 9: 429 - 448*

SOCIO-CULTURAL ASPECTS

FEMALE SEX-ROLE CONFLICTS AND EATING DISORDERS.

Josine Arondeus & Winny Weeda-Mannak

It is a consistent finding from clinical and epidemiological research that eating disorders occur more commonly in females than males and usually develop around puberty and adolescence (Herzog & Copeland, 1985; Szmukler, 1985). The convincing evidence that anorexia and bulimia nervosa are overrepresented in females has resulted in various postulations that socio-cultural factors may be important determinants in the expression of eating disorders. The purpose of this chapter is to review some of the important socio-cultural variables considered to be predisposing factors to the expression of anorexia or bulimia nervosa.

Contemporary symbols of fashion

Concepts of feminine beauty have varied through history. Throughout centuries different body shapes have been selected for, and associated with, desirable social virtues (Schwartz & Thompson, 1980). Particularly during the last decades a shift towards leanness and thinness for women could be observed in Western societies and has been linked to a possible increase in the prevalence of eating disorders (Selvini-Palazolli, 1974; Boskind-Lodahl, 1976; Bruch, 1978). Ryle, (1939) probably was the first one who emphasised how the social pressure of the slimming fashion may provide a general increase of anorexia nervosa. More recently Bruch, (1978) has referred to the increase of anorexia nervosa as "an epidemic illness the spread of which may be attributed to psycho-sociological factors". Contemporary cultural fashion has valued thinness as a symbol of beauty, sexual attractiveness and success, while weight control is held synonymous for discipline, personal strength and willpower. The change of idealised female shape has been documented and quantified by Garner et al., (1980) who have collected data from several sources including Playboy Magazine and Miss America Pageants. While the cultural pressure to be thin has been persistently reflected in magazines, movies and television, evidence has indicated that the average women has become heavier over the past decades. The impact of this unsolvable conflict between cultural demands and biological forces is illustrated by the increased pervasiveness of dieting among women (Garner et al., 1980). Hence it is not surprising that eating disorders have been viewed as cultural phenomena, so called "metaphors for our time" (Orbach, 1986). Through times women have learnt that social acceptance is directly related to physical appearance and that looking attractive is an essential criterion of value for women (Wooley & Wooley, 1985). The association of thinness with desirable social status has been considered a significant predisposing factor to the expression of eating disorders, especially affecting vulnerable adolescents who have come to believe that weight control is equal to self-discipline and self-worth (Bruch, 1978).

Thinness as a symbol of social and sexual freedom

In the early 1960s the image of a slim, long legged and small breasted body shape was promoted by appearance of a mannequin named the "Shrimp", who broke with the contemporary voluptuous images of women (Orbach, 1986). However the ideal of thinness was to symbolise other aspects of change as well. It could be understood as a rejection of the constraints inherent to social class and sex, an attempt to transcend barriers between class, age and sex. Bennett & Gurin, (1982) have suggested that the shift from the 'maternal figure', retaining body fat, to the thin body standard symbolises the expression of female sexual liberation, where slimness has been opposed to fertility: "the central expression of the new liberated women was her thin body, which came to symbolise athleticism, nonreproductive sexuality and a kind of androgynous independence". Beck et al. (1976) have supported the assumed association between the preference for a thinner body shape and a less traditional feminine sex-role affiliation. They found that women who preferred a smaller overall shape were less traditionally feminine.

Successful femininity: the exclusion of 'masculine' virtues.

For young women, developing femininity successfully requires the meeting of three essential demands: deference to other people, converting one's own needs to those of others and seeking self definition through affiliation (Orbach, 1986). Traditionally girls have been taught that other people's needs are more important than their own and in this way are encouraged to deny and suppress their own inner needs. As a consequence women have not been able to develop an authentic sense of entitlement for their desires. Hence they will not be able to experience themselves as people with entitled wants, feelings and needs. Anorexia nervosa has been understood as an exaggerated form of the denial of the cultures values for women while at the same time as a protest against the cultural rules that constrain a woman's life (Orbach, 1986). The unfamiliarity with one's own inner sensations, as well as the preoccupation with other people's needs, results in a sense of self that has become dependent upon the approval of those to whom they must defer. The self esteem of anorexic patients has appeared to be extremely dependent upon interpersonal approval and social recognition (Bruch, 1974). Boskind-Lodahl, (1976) found clinical evidence to contend that women with eating disorders have internalised the cultural standards of successful femininity in a desperate attempt to avoid social rejection. Data to support these postulations have been found in a recent study of Weeda-Mannak & Arondeus, (1990) who found that anorectic women have less self esteem than non eating disordered female controls and that lack of self esteem appeared to be associated with greater femininity. According to Bardwick, (1971) all women from an early age tend to be rewarded socially for affiliation, resulting in their self esteem being strongly tied to interpersonal approval. The ideal of femininity has almost always excluded the attribution of so called 'masculine' virtues such as independence, effectiveness and the expression of emotions such as aggression and anger (Wooley & Wooley, 1985). Women with anorexia nervosa have been found to particularly shape their life in the cultural expectations of femininity and have failed to adopt traditionally masculine attributes (Sitnick & Katz, 1984; Weeda-Mannak & Arondeus, 1990). When compared to a matched control group of non eating disordered women anorectic and bulimic women were found to score significantly higher on femininity while scoring significantly lower on masculinity. Feministic theorists have identified the socio-cultural environment as an important transmitter of an inferior psychology of women, contributing to the development of mental disorder in women in general and of eating disorders in particular (Boskind-Lodahl, 1986; Orbach, 1986).

Contradictory role definitions for women.

It was Selvini-Palazolli, (1974) who originally linked the expression of anorexia nervosa to the new, often contradictory roles for women in modern society. She emphasised that the cultural and social changes such as the admission of women into traditional male preserves such as education and professional careers while previously confined to the role of housewife and mother, tend to aggravate the inner conflicts of women. "Today, in fact, women are expected to be beautiful, smart and well groomed, and to devote a great deal of time to their personal appearance even while competing in business and the professions. They must have a career and yet be romantic, tender and sweet and in marriage play the part of the ideal wife cum mistress and cum mother who puts away her hard earned diplomas to wash nappies and perform other menial chores" (p. 35). The changing female sex-role definitions have implied that women are not only supposed to adopt traditional feminine traits but traditional masculine characteristics too. In this respect becoming a female adult might be more difficult than becoming a male adult. According to Selvini-Palazolli, (1974) it is quite obvious that the social pressure to satisfy so many contradictory demands has considerably contributed to unsolvable conflicts in women; especially in those who have adopted a traditional feminine identity, while at the same time incorporating more modern standards for vocational achievement. For many women overwhelmed by the fear of losing control in the face of such demands, weight control represents control in other ways of personal functioning. In a number of studies it has been found that women with eating disorders display a more than average drive for achievement (Garner et al., 1983; Weeda-Mannak et al., 1983). One might expect that women with an increased drive to achieve will enter traditionally male preserves such as higher education and careers. These competitive environments usually demand the adoption of traditional masculine traits such as competitiveness, aggression and initiative. Within this context a women lacking those masculine attributes can only fail either by performing inadequately or by feeling guilty about succeeding. Bardwick, (1971) has also contended that women are not only expected to achieve in a highly competitive vocational world, but also to excel in traditional feminine roles. The sex-typed traits that were reinforced in female childhood are quite different from the attributes needed for successful vocational careers. According to Bardwick (1971) because of the link between the changing body shape at puberty and the intensification of role conflicts for women the body has become the focal point to cope with conflicting achievement and psychosocial demands.

Conclusions

The clinical as well as epidemiological finding of the overrepresentation of eating disorders among women has been held as the most convincing support for the view that socio-cultural factors contribute to the expression of anorexia and bulimia nervosa. In this chapter the importance of female sex-role identity, within the context of other biological and psychological factors which are believed to play a role in the pathogenesis of eating disorders, has been highlighted. Since not all women are suffering from an eating disorder it would be naïve to assume that cultural factors alone can 'cause' the development of an eating disorder. However there is a widespread belief, particularly among feministic contributors, that there is a continuity in all women's experience which makes them vulnerable for the manifestation of anorexia or bulimia nervosa (Orbach, 1986; Wooley & Wooley, 1985). In this respect it is important to stress the significance of the social-cultural environment in transmitting a psychology for women which tends to deny their biological characteristics, their rights and their needs and makes them believe that denial of selfhood is a symbol of self-worth and autonomy.

REFERENCES

Bardwick J. (1971) *Psychology of women: A study of bio-cultural conflicts.* New York: Harper and Row.

Beck S.B., Ward-Hull C.I., McLear P.M. (1976) Variables related to women's somatic preferences of the male and female body. *Journal of Personality and Social Psychology 34:1200-1210.*

Bennett W.B. & Gurin J. (1982) *The dieter's dilemma: Eating less and weighing more.* New York: Basis Books.

Boskind-Lodahl M. (1976) Cinderella's step-sisters: A feminist perspective on anorexia nervosa and bulimia. *Signs: Journal of Women in Culture and Society 2:342-256.*

Bruch H. (1978) *The Golden Cage.* Cambridge: Harvard University Press.

Garner D.M., Garfinkel P.E., Schwarz D., Thompson M. (1980) Cultural expectations of thinness in women. *Psychological Reports 47:483-491.*

Garner D.M., Olmsted M.P., Polivy J., Garfinkel P.E. (1983) Does anorexia nervosa occur on a continuum ? Subgroups of weight-preoccupied women and their relationship to anorexia nervosa. *International Journal of Eating Disorders 2:11-20.*

Herzog D.B. & Copeland P.M. (1985) Eating disorders. *New England Journal of Medicine 5:295-303.*

Orbach S. (1986) *Hunger strike. The anorectic's struggle as a metaphor for our age.* New York/London: Norton & Company.

Ryle J.A. (1939) Discussion on anorexia nervosa. *Proceedings of Royal Society Medicine 32:735-737.*

Selvini-Palazolli M.P. (1974) *Self-starvation. From the intra-psychic to the transpersonal approach to anorexia nervosa.* London: Chaucer Publishing Co.

Sitnick T. & Katz J.L. (1984) Sex role identity and anorexia nervosa. *International Journal of Eating Disorders 3:81-89.*

Szmukler G.I. (1985) The epidemiology of anorexia nervosa and bulimia. *Journal of Psychiatric Research 19:143- 153.*

Weeda-Mannak W.L., Drop M.J., Smits F., Strijbosch L.W. & Bremer J.J. (1983) Toward an early recognition of anorexia nervosa. *International Journal of Eating Disorders 2:27-37.*

Weeda-Mannak W.L., Arondeus J.M. & Takens R.J. (1990) Sex-role identity and anorexia nervosa. In: Drenth J.D., Sergeant J.A. and Takens R.J. (Eds). *European perspectives in psychology.* Vol 2. Chicester: Wiley & Sons.

Wooley S.C. & Wooley O.W. (1985) Intensive outpatient and residential treatment for bulimia. In: Garner D.M. & Garfinkel P.E. (Eds). *Handbook of psychotherapy for anorexia nervosa and bulimia.* New York/London: Guilford Press.

THE RELATIONSHIP BETWEEN DAUGHTERS AND MOTHERS AND BULIMIA NERVOSA

Karin Bell

The life-history of a bulimic woman is traced up to the outbreak of her symptoms. Several aspects of female development which promote the beginnings of a bulimia syndrome are expounded with the help of this case example. The ultimate triggering of the syndrome is the adolescent problem of dissolution of emotional ties, which the patient is unable to cope with due to earlier shortcomings in her strivings towards autonomy. In detail, this means excessive stimulation in the early mother-daughter relationship which renders it impossible for the infant to withdraw. The daughter cannot cope appropriately with the rapprochement phase, since she identifies with a dependent mother who reacts anxiously towards her daughter's independence. The daughter develops the same ego ideal as her mother, that of a "mother who is only good". Certain specifically female caring attitudes and aggressive inhibitions are "inherited" as a result. All in all, the family atmosphere is chaotic and offers little security, with no clear boundaries between the generations and with the 'parentising' of the children. The girl is given no affirmation of her female sexuality, while the father, often an alcoholic, tries to seduce her into dependence on him. Changes in cultural expectations are also mentioned: the self-sacrificing woman was the ideal of Western societies up to the end of the '60s. The growing demand for female independence after that intensifies the specifically female conflict between loyalty to a relationship and autonomy.

Martha:

Martha is 17 years old. Enrolled for therapy by her mother, she is also brought to therapy by her mother. Both mother and daughter leave it up to me at first to decide whether I want to see them together or separately. Martha cannot make up her mind when asked what she would like, so that we stand wavering in the hall for a while. In the end the mother decides: "I'll go, so that you can relate your worries undisturbed for once."

In 1980, in the 3rd edition of the Diagnostic and Statistical Manual of Mental Disorders (DSM III), bulimia nervosa was defined as a syndrome in its own right and differentiated from anorexia nervosa. The symptom of morbid hunger attacks with or without subsequent self-induced vomiting has, admittedly, already been described within the context of other illnesses: however, the bulimia syndrome has only emerged in the stricter sense of a differentiated new form of eating disorder since the '60s and '70s. A sudden rise in the number of patients in the '80s would seem to suggest an epidemic. This "epidemic" probably began in the late '40s. The breeding-ground: a post-war affluent society in which success, performance and food played a large part and were interlinked in many different ways. As bulimia nervosa is a sex-linked illness - 95% of sufferers are women - it is natural to seek culturally-linked causes of the illness in the changing conceptions of the female sex as described, for example, by Schmauch (1987) for the Federal Republic of Germany. After the war sexual division of labour was re-established in a relatively rigid form: "Mothers were almost always there, like a natural and inevitable unity of love and control, or they were absent, and the separation meant guilt and distress" (Schmauch, 1987, p.39). Tension arose between the ideal of mother and housewife and the wish or necessity for a career of one's own, frequently described as "making money on the side", which conveyed itself to the daughters as a message to be both like their mothers and to become their opposites. More possibilities seem to present themselves to women from around 1970 onwards. Unfortunately, this new freedom very quickly turned into demands made upon women by society "the professed conception of modern women requires that she is capable of integrating incompatible restraints and interests, fully in command of the situation" (Schmauch, loc. cit. p.40). Mitscherlich-Nielsen (1978) outlines the situation as follows: "Role expectations in society are beginning to flounder more and more... conflicting demands are beginning to make themselves felt: women are supposed to learn to make themselves independent in our culture, while at the same time they are unable to exploit any opportunities of freedom, since the necessary family, professional and psychological conditions required for this are lacking."

"This makes them feel quite worthless. They are supposed to be empathic mothers, fully understanding the complicated psychological problems of their children, make good house-wives and, what is more, be equal partners to their husbands, also capable of asserting themselves professionally. These are demands hardly anyone can meet." (p.688)

Habermas (1990) is also of the opinion that one of the historical preconditions for bulimia is to be found in the changing roles of the sexes. So long as women define themselves essentially through and in their relationship with the male sex, their independence remains such in appearance only. The relatively new, seemingly contradictory, expectation put on young women to be independent for the other sex (ie most important, it would seem, is that they appear to be independent), which becomes more apparent when analysing advertising than in social-psychological studies, fits in with the physical ideal that slimness equates to attractiveness for others and autonomy. "......new, at least regarding it's universal propagation in Western society, ...is the clear association of a slim body and the autonomy it symbolises with the ideal of sexual attractiveness, which threatens to betray that autonomy" (Habermas, 1990, p.205).

The finding of one's own identity and the dissolution of emotional ties with the primary family are adolescent tasks in the maturation process which occupy the typical bulimic woman during the beginnings of the symptom complex. The following chapter will discuss those patients whose symptom complex first appears within the framework of adolescent conflicts in the process of gaining emotional freedom. I shall not refer to patients who develop bulimic symptoms in the course of other neurotic illnesses, nor to those patients with a borderline personality structure.

> *Martha has suffered from morbid hunger attacks for two years. These seldom result in self- induced vomiting, so that, she has put on about 5kg. She is not very overweight though, as she is basically tall and stately, and is rather plump at most. When she was only 10 or 11 years old she did think that she was too fat, although she was slim then. She went on a starvation diet for a while but never became as slim as she had wanted to. Two years ago she had to break off a stay abroad prematurely. Since her return she has been suffering from binge eating attacks several times a week, when she has to keep on eating until she 'has the feeling that she will burst'. She then gives a typical account: repeated attempts to lose weight through rigorous dieting, fear of losing control in a morbid hunger attack, while at the same time thoughts of food occupy her mind as soon as she has some peace and quiet.*

With the help of Martha's life-history, I shall attempt to trace certain stages of development and highlight factors which could promote the beginnings of bulimia. At the same time I shall mention certain development crises specific to womanhood.

Development into womanhood begins with sex determination at birth.

On the one hand this view, held in particular by Stoller and Kleeman, stresses the influence of cognitive maturation processes on development sexual identity. Sex determination at birth initiates a socialisation process which teaches the girl that she is feminine, as well as how and in what areas a female family member (and the part of society her family represents) should act. (Kleeman, 1977). On the other hand, prime importance is attached to environmental influences. (Stoller, 1977)

When the girl begins to feel like a girl on the basis of sex determination imparted to her through her environment, she models herself on her mother. Her aim then is to apply this model, to examine it and to develop herself in her own way. This separation from the mother and its flexible implementation is a difficult task in adolescence. The outcome is frequently obdurate separation: "I am not at all like my mother", or an identity diffusion, whereby differences between mother and daughter are hardly noticed: "We are like two sisters." Martha's model is a woman who only feels satisfied when she has a baby to look after. Martha was born when her older sister reached the age of puberty. She was the youngest child, but only because her father denied her mother the wish to have more children. Now that Martha has finally picked up the courage to

begin therapy, there is another baby in the family: Her mother is looking after her sister's child. Although this baby is only six months old, her sister is already planning a second child "so that everything doesn't centre around the baby". One has the impression that the family needs the external reality of a second baby in order to keep the baby at a suitable distance.

When Martha was 3 years old her father was made unemployed. Her mother looked for a job, which was first experienced as guilty and painful separation, but later continued, although the external necessity no longer existed. A certain ambivalent attitude on the side of Martha's mother became apparent here with regard to her feminine self-definition: to be a woman means to be a mother.

Results of infant observation in the past few years have changed our conception of infant capabilities and demonstrated subtleties in the co-ordination of the relationship between mother and child hitherto unknown. Although it is true that Winnicott, (1974), with his differentiation between the 'holding mother' and object mother, has already demonstrated two different maternal offerings of relationship which correspond to the various relationship desires in infants in various 'states'. Brazelton (1983) stresses the significance of rhythmic sequences in the relationship between mother and child, whereby states of withdrawal and receptiveness to stimuli must alternate. Martha describes most impressively the unrest and hectic pace at home which arises because the baby is experienced as someone to whom one has to devote a great deal of one's time. The result is probably a chaotic over-stimulation, which means that peaceful phases of privacy and inward contemplation cannot be experienced. This could depict a basal prerequisite for obsessive and impulsive behaviour.

The rapprochement phase as a critical period in female development of identity.

Girls begin to describe themselves as girls at the age of 15 months: an identification process with female characteristics now begins, for which the mother serves as a model. At the same time in the rapprochement phase development of an identity separate from that of the mother begins to take place. Chodorow (1974) accentuates the significance of the relationship for female identity development, which results from the fact that separation from the mother is not necessary for the development of female identity. I consider it a specifically female task to find a sphere appropriate to one's own needs for the relationship to the mother and separation from her. As independence is a culturally positively rated term at the moment, yet women cannot follow culturally pre-set standards here as they are not intended for women in this form. Woman's independence, after all, is supposed to provide a function in the relationship which takes the load off and at the same time attracts the man.

During the rapprochement phase certain forms of toilet training can arouse doubts in the child as to whether it has command of its own body or whether the body belongs to the mother. This feeling is intensified through budding, possibly forbidden, masturbation around this time. Thus proneness to disturbances abounds. There are mothers who reject in this phase and mothers who monopolize. Whatever the case, it is a turbulent period, demanding a great deal of stamina in self-confidence from mothers, for they are, in quick succession, both the object of clinging affection and the object of rejection. As the mother relives her relationship toward her own mother in her relationship with her daughter, she also relives her own painful separation and individualisation. That puts a strain on her as the mother relives again the "loss of her own mother and the loss of her baby" (Bergmann, 1982).

> *Martha cannot recount anything from this period. She was considered to be a well-behaved, rather anxious child who had problems coping with the separation of going to kindergarten. Toilet training was unproblematic, and there were no stubborn phases. It is precisely the inconspicuousness of this phase which would seem to us to be an indication of a possible disturbance. Martha's mother is anxious when the children leave the house and always wants to know where they are. In addition, she 'does not appear to be able to live without a baby'. Thus it is unlikely that she could understand Martha's wish to 'move away' from her. It seems that Martha has adapted herself to the anxieties of her mother, who could not endure separation.*

A further indication of the difficulties Martha's mother has with separation and individualisation is that she returned to her own mother's house shortly after her marriage and has lived closely together with her mother ever since. What is more, she dissipates her energies on various external demands, and can hardly bring her own plans to an end. It is thus doubtful whether Martha' mother experienced 'the loss of her baby and the loss of her mother' in the rapprochement phase. On the contrary, her behaviour would make it seem that she is continually trying to avert experiences of separation and loss. Thus Martha cannot develop any aggression in her gaining of independence. Instead, when she sees how her mother is worn out by the demands of others, but at the same time repeatedly offers to spoil them, she will experience an inner conflict as to what she wants from her mother. On the one hand, she isn't supposed to become independent, while on the other hand she no longer wishes to burden her mother. This dilemma frequently crops up as a transference/countertransference constellation in therapy sessions with bulimic patients: the passive demanding attitude results in the therapist unthinkingly becoming more active. This caring attention does not satisfy the patient, however. Behind the passivity lies a claim to independence.

In Martha's family the climate is also such that differences and separation are to a large extent dispensed with. External and internal boundaries merge into one. On the one hand, the family has no outward private life, the door is always open, while on the other hand there is no inner private life: friends, clothes, personal feelings, and sexual experiences are shared by the women in the family, with the father the only outsider. And so the contours between mother and daughter, already more difficult to define because they are the same sex, become blurred.

Those inherent tendencies in the girl which lead to separation individualisation problems are intensified by an ego-ideal which upholds the conception of an "ideal mother".

According to Jacobson (1978), ego-identifications with realistic parental images arise in girls when the aims and attainment norms of the parents are adopted. The girl then identifies herself in particular with the mother. Unavoidable or avoidable frustration through the mother leads to primitive ideal images of the self and the love objects turning into a unified ego-ideal, which ties on to the grandiose desires of the preoedipal child and its belief in parental omnipotence. Thus a sacrificing and caring ideal is formed in women, in which any experience of separation-individualisation or realisation of their own interests following a phase of intensive mothering (eg., when a brother or sister is born or the mother goes out to work), contribute to the formation of this ideal if the familiar climate offers no possibility for dealing with the disappointment it arouses in the child.

In Martha's case the mother went back to work when she was three years old. Martha's mother is the eldest of a family of six. She felt forced to take over responsibility for her younger brothers and sisters at an early age, as her mother suffered from depressive moods and her father died when she was 15 years old. She was thus forced into early independence which, however, instead of furthering her own strivings towards autonomy, became independence 'for others'.

Martha's mother is to a great extent committed to an excessive, motherly ego-ideal, including its negative individuation in favour of caring for others: she cannot handle disappointment and rage, which she does not experience as necessary developmental steps, but as a questioning of her motherly capabilities, with the result that she passes on her own aggressive inhibitions to her daughter.

The oedipal phase can only be adequately overcome if there is sufficient separation from the mother.

While attention has hitherto been directed to the relationship between Martha and her mother, I shall now describe her relationship with her brother and her father, which presents itself like a negative of the afore-mentioned relationship between the two women. While the women have a "really good" relationship, the men are more or less left out in the cold. The father is consciously left out of things, the brother keeps himself out of things. In Martha's eyes her father, and his drinking in particular, is to blame for her mother's unhappiness.

Usually rather quiet and withdrawn, he becomes loud when he has been drinking and reproaches her mother. Martha thinks everything would be okay if the father didn't drink, and in a way she is right, if the father in his fondness for drink is interpreted as a symbol of the inadequate attempts of the whole family to free themselves of emotional ties.

Father and daughter had a very close relationship until puberty set in. They used to exchange a lot of affection, which Martha sensed her father didn't get enough of from her mother. Since reaching the age of puberty, Martha has been on her mother's side and avoids any physical contact with her father.

Incestuous anxieties reactivated through puberty suggest themselves here as the cause of estrangement between father and daughter. Martha is probably afraid to steer her father's seductive overtures, owing to her lack of separation individuation abilities. She was particularly offended, however, by disparaging remarks from her father about her body in adolescence. Emphasis has often been put on the importance of the father for the development of positive female sexuality, but the mother can also play a positively strengthening role if she encourages her daughter towards development into a sexually perceptive woman. However, Martha's mother seems to have given up as far as her own sexual attractiveness is concerned: she also thinks of herself as too fat, ie, unattractive, and has retreated into the role of the caring mother.

The 30 year old brother - thin, like his father - still lives in the primary family as well. There is an incestuous touch to her relationship with him, with frequent exchanges of physical affection. One would think Martha was in love with him when she speaks of him. The brother, however, also appears to be a substitute husband for the mother in the sense of the blurred borderlines between the generations in this family.

Although her brother's acknowledgement of her femininity is important for and beneficial to Martha's female identity, the close relationship between the two (who differ greatly in age) seems like an attempt to reconcile desires appropriate to their age for a heterosexual relationship, ie., strivings towards dissolution of emotional ties with the primary family and the desire to bind to the family. A trans-generational passing on of unsolved autonomy conflicts is thus to be found on both the female and the male side.

With the women in the family, these show themselves in eating disorders and/or depression: Martha's grandmother was overweight - she now has diabetes mellitus - and suffered from depression as well. Martha's mother has weight problems, and there are signs of neurotic depression (inner unrest, state of exhaustion), Martha herself has bulimia. The three women are both united and divided through cooking and eating. The grandmother is envious of the others since she has had to stick to a diet. Although the mother considers herself too fat, she cannot summon up the energy to go on a diet and her cooking is rich in calories. Martha has been trying to lose weight since she reached puberty and would like most of all 'her and her mother to lose weight together.' Working from the basis of similar inner conflicts in the three women, the obvious question would seem to be why Martha has fallen ill with bulimia, of all things. Recognition of bulimia as an illness has undoubtedly played a part in this, providing Martha with a frame for a compromisable solution to her conflicts. Further external factors are the increasing affluence of a family which was still poor in the grandmother's and in the mother's day and a greater demand for self-control of oral impulses, compared to the days when "the way to a man's heart was through his stomach".

On the male side, increased alcohol consumption and/or uncontrolled impulsiveness are to be found.

Eating disorders have two-sided beginnings. Possible causes of the disorder, and how they can occur in early childhood have hitherto been described. The changes which occurred in puberty have already been portrayed in Martha's relationship with her father.

The sex-linked separation-individuation conflicts between mother and daughter normally flare up again in puberty 'until they can leave each other alone'. Not with Martha, however: when puberty begins to set in she has a brief anorexic phase, like those not uncommonly found in young girls. At the same time, however, Martha begins to identify completely with the cares and troubles of her mother. She is upset and sad that her mother 'lets people exploit her to the full'. Whenever the tries to assert herself aggressively against her mother, she feels guilty and as bad as the father she runs down. Instead of the forthcoming emotional freedom, an intensified bond results in which Martha seems to sense vaguely that something isn't quite right. And so when she was 15 years old she decided to live abroad for a while 'to get away from home for once'. Having resolved not to let herself be spoilt any more, she rejected the possibly excessively caring nature of her guest family in an extremely undiplomatic manner, which led to conflicts with them: an attempt at emotional freedom with the wrong object. The bulimic symptoms have been there since her return. Habermas (1990) describes the family background of the bulimic patient as offering little security, and burdened with a great deal of open conflicts. Thus the patient prematurely takes on an adult role in early adolescence, a well as responsibility for other members of the family. Greater efforts have to be made to ward off regressive desires, and independence has to be secured by way of rigid self-control. Satisfaction of regressive needs ensues by way of altruistic withdrawal (A. Freud, 1936).

The patients pay a high price for this since their desire 'to be there for others' is maintained by unconscious motives which serve to ward off separation anxieties, conflicting strivings must be kept from being perceived. This leads to aggressive strivings, even harmless ones such as the desire for a room of one's own, only being perceived as vague and confused inner tension, not able to be named. The bulimic patient tries to dispel this inner tension in a binge eating attack and in doing so threatens anew her modest self-image. The symbolic function of eating is frequently referred to, whereby the binge eating is portrayed as an unsuccessful attempt to embody the mother, only to eject her in the subsequent vomiting. This moving towards and moving away from the mother in the rapprochement phase was thus repeated regressively on an oral level. Martha's life history and that of other bulimic women does not rule out an interpretation of this kind. Along with the symbolic significance, however, eating would also appear to be an aid to removing inner tension and feelings of emptiness which occur in these women because they have never experienced their inner sphere as something separate from the mother. Perception of their libidinal and aggressive strings is therefore greatly lacking, and so they cannot search for possible solutions.

Most women, however, are familiar with the conflicts which subject bulimic patients to failure. The conflict between the loyalty which regulates a relationship and legitimate separation aggression is intensified by changing cultural expectations and ideals. Many women know the ego-ideal of a mother who is only good, who sacrifices her own desires. They more or less cope with the rapprochement phase, whereby identification with the 'separation' side of the mother, which would make their own autonomy easier, seldom occurs.

I conclude my thoughts with perhaps a rather individual interpretation of the tale of 'Rumpelstiltskin'. In Rumpelstiltskin, I see in the king's daughter (who was not acknowledged because she was not named) that wild, aggressively demanding part of her self. It is not until she succeeds in integrating this part of her, and only when she can stop fulfilling father's (and mother's) ridiculous wish to spin gold out of straw, that she can become creative and fruitful.

REFERENCES

Bergmann, A. (1982) Considerations about the Development of the Girl during Separation-Individuation Process in Mendell, D. (Ed) *Early Female Development.* Lancaster: MPT

Brazelton, B.T. (1983) Precursors for the Development of Emotions in Early Infancy. In R. Plutchik & H. Kellerman (Eds.) *Emotion: Theory, Research and Experience, Vol.2: Emotions in Early Development.* New York: Academic Press

Chodorow, N. (1974) Family Structure and Feminine Personality. In Rosaldo, MZ., Lamphere, L. (Eds) *Women, Culture and Society.* Stanford: University Press

Freud, A. (1936) *Das Ich und die Abwehrmechanismen.* München: Kindler

Habermas, T. (1990) *Heißhunger*. Frankfurt: Fischer

Jacobson, E. (1978) *Das Selbst und die Welt der Objekte.* Frankfurt: Suhrkamp

Kleeman, J.A. (1977) Freud's Views on Early Female Sexuality in the Light of Direct Child Observation. Blum, H.P.(Ed) *Female Psychology.* N.York: IUP

Mitscherlich-Nielsen, M. (1978) *Zur Psychoanalyse der Weiblichkeit.* Psyche 32, p.669-694
Schmauch, U. (1987) *Anatomie und Schicksal.* Frankfurt: Fischer
Stoller, R.S. (1977) Primary Feminity in Blum, H.P. (Ed) *Female Psychology.* New York: IUP
Winnicot, D.W. (1974) *Reifungsprozesse und fördernde* Umwelt. Stuttgart: Klett

SEXUAL EXPERIENCES

EATING PATTERNS AND UNWANTED SEXUAL EXPERIENCES.

Rachel Calam and Peter Slade

There is an increasing debate in the literature concerning the extent to which unwanted sexual experiences may play some part in the aetiology of eating disorders. While most reports generally look at presence or absence of abuse, it may be that specific types of experience are of particular significance, or may have a particularly damaging effect. This chapter describes two studies of women in therapy for an eating disorder, and compares their responses to a Sexual Events Questionnaire (SEQ) to those obtained from women in therapy for mood disorder, and to women with no known history of eating disorder. Particular categories of sexual experience appeared to be of importance in the eating disorder groups. In particular, sexual experience with a close male relative was reported more frequently. The paper discusses the ways in which unwanted sexual experiences may contribute to the development of an eating disorder.

There has been some debate in the literature recently over the question of whether women who have experienced sexual abuse or unwanted sexual experiences of some kind may be more likely to develop difficulties associated with eating. Some studies appear to indicate the possibility of a link between unwanted sexual experience and the later development of an eating disorder (Abraham & Beumont, 1982; Oppenheimer et al., 1985; Palmer et al., 1990). However a study by Lacey, (1990) has not provided support for this hypothesis.

Some studies of non-clinic women (Calam & Slade, 1987; Beckman & Burns, 1990) have indicated that unwanted sexual experience may be associated with the development of problems associated with eating, as measured by self-report questionnaire, but other studies (Finn et al., 1986) have not supported this association. These authors have suggested that rather than tapping a real association between eating difficulties and unwanted sexual experience, what is happening is that both occur with such high rates in the female population as a whole and so there is a high probability that many women will have experienced both. Therefore, the evidence for a link is not clear.

For those women who have experienced unwanted sexual advances, the link is sometimes plain. Calam and Slade (1989) reported the perceptions of a group of women who had experienced a range of unwanted sexual encounters and who drew clear links between these and their subsequent development of a full-blown eating disorder. A common theme was that these women had lost control of their lives in some sense following the unwanted experience and the eating disorder permitted them some sense of regained control. Some women reported a desire to alter their body shape in order to avoid further sexual approaches. Others talked about their feelings of guilt, disgust, and self-hatred and said that their binge eating and vomiting in some sense formed a punishment for what they had experienced. Some of these women clearly thought that they had brought the abuse upon themselves. Others talked of parallels between their appetite for food and their appetite for sex. For these women gaining control of the appetite meant taking control of their sexual urges as well. A particularly striking feature for most of the women was that the unwanted sexual experience had often taken place at the time of other major problems and upheavals in their lives. Looking at these women's comments it is possible to draw up models of the ways in which unwanted sexual experience might lead to eating disorder. A rather straightforward model is presented in Figure 1.

Figure 1:

A LINEAR MODEL FOR THE TRANSLATION OF THE EXPERIENCE OF ABUSE INTO AN EATING DISORDER

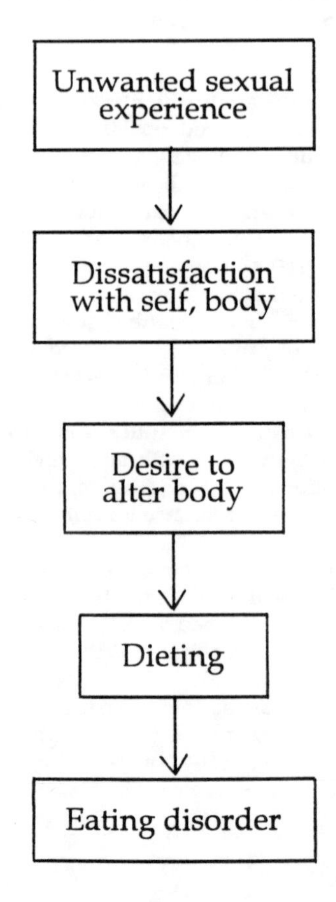

In this linear model, the experience of abuse or other unwanted sexual experience leads to dissatisfaction with one's self and body, leading in turn to a desire to alter the body in some way and hence to dieting and subsequently to eating disorder. However Calam and Slade hypothesized that intrafamilial abuse might be associated specifically with anorexic symptomatology as self-starvation might act as a form of punishment toward an abusing parent or a parent who had failed to protect the woman from abuse from another family member. In this model (see Figure 2) some aspect of family interaction would make the individual more prone to abuse and also fuel a need to attain control over the family situation. In this setting, a change in eating patterns might become functional as a means of attaining control and hence lead on to the development of an eating disorder.

Figure 2:

A CIRCULAR HYPOTHESIS FOR THE RELATIONSHIP BETWEEN THE EXPERIENCE OF ABUSE AND EATING DISORDERS

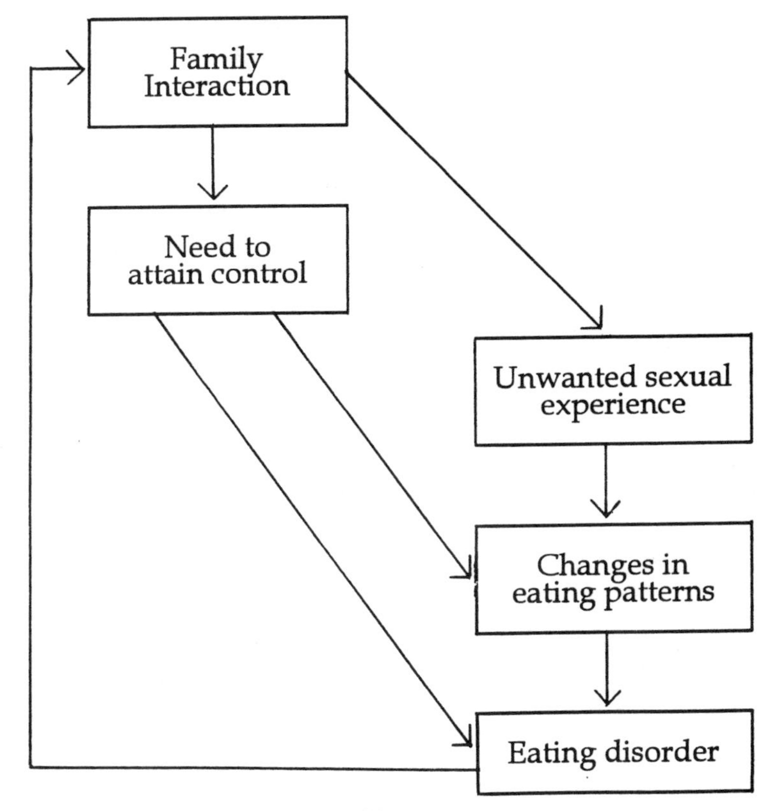

'Sexual Events' survey

To assess the extent to which unwanted sexual experience might contribute to the development of eating disorder we studied 49 women in therapy for eating disorders and a group of 60 female undergraduate students. All women completed a Sexual Events Questionnaire (SEQ) which asks about various sexual experiences, the age at which they occurred, and their impact on the respondent at the time. Using chi-square analysis, we found that women with eating disorders were significantly more likely to report having been upset by having someone expose their genitals to them (36% vs. 16%), more likely to have experienced forced sexual intercourse (30% vs. 15%), and more likely to have had a sexual experience with an authority figure (16% vs. 3%). They were also more likely to have had a sexual experience with a close male relative (20% vs. 5%). There was no difference between women with anorectic or bulimic symptoms.

In a second study in North America we compared a group of 37 eating disordered women with a group of 20 women with mood disorders attending a clinic. Again, it was found that the women with eating disorders were more likely to have been upset by having someone expose their genitals to them (32% vs. 5%). The women in the eating disorder group were also more likely to have had sexual contact with a close male relative (27% vs. 5%).

Overall the clinic groups reported more experiences of forced intercourse (30%, UK, 26%, USA) than did the students (15%) and higher incidence of actual or attempted rape (16%, UK, 14%,USA, 7%, students). The mood disorder patients reported a similar frequency of sexual contact with a close male relative to that reported by the students.

The data reported here would seem to indicate that propensity to report specific sexual experiences notably exposure, forced intercourse, sexual contact with an authority figure and sexual contact with a close male relative is more likely in women with eating disorders than those without. Moreover it would appear that it is particularly the experience of unwanted exposure and the experience of sexual contact with a close male relative which distinguishes women with eating disorder from women with mood disorder. Hence, although it might be anticipated that sexual contact within the family might have a globally disturbing and upsetting effect upon the individual, this did not appear to be the case. The women in the mood disorder sample were reporting rates of intrafamilial experience no higher than the comparison group. This might lead to the conclusion that there is something specific about contact within the family that might give rise to an eating disorder.

Clearly there are difficulties in interpreting data of this kind. The data are retrospective accounts given by questionnaire. With respect to exposure for example it may be that the women with eating disorder have a high level of sensitivity to any kind of exposure, so that which might be quite tolerable for a woman whose body image is not disturbed may be rated as distressing by a woman for whom bodily appearance and sexuality are of themselves extremely disturbing. It is also important to note that Calam and Slade's hypothesis that intrafamilial abuse might lead specifically to anorexic symptomatology is simply not held up by the data. This might lead to more general hypotheses about the effects of abuse within the family. Hence for some women with anorexic symptomatology it may be that their eating disorder has become functional in "turning off" the abuse while for others their bulimia might reflect an overall sense of disturbance and distress over the use that has been made of their bodies which might lead to very different hypotheses about loss of control and the subsequent development of bulimic symptomatology. Hence it may be the case that while giving a message to the family about the abuse has some part to play in the symptomatology it is not the whole of the picture. Indeed in order for an eating disorder to develop it is probable that a whole range of setting conditions are necessary (Slade, 1982).

It may be most appropriate to think of abuse or unwanted sexual experience of some kind as one of a number of possible setting conditions contributing to the overall development of the eating disorder. Figure 3 presents a model which offers hypotheses about some of the processes which may be involved in the development of an eating disorder where abuse or unwanted sexual experience is present.

The unwanted sexual experience is seen as leading to several things: to a need to establish control over the environment; to emotional change within the individual and also to changes in eating patterns. Research on children who report sexual abuse very frequently indicates that their eating patterns may change at least in the short term and food refusal may be common (Peters, 1976). Each of these factors will interact with personality factors of the kind that Slade (1982) describes and may also have some effect upon interaction within the family. As mentioned earlier the women who we have interviewed report that there are often other problems or major changes and upheavals going on in their lives at the particular time that the unwanted experience took place and it may be that, within the setting conditions that these help to create, the change in eating patterns becomes functional. This helps the woman to feel in control of things and may simultaneously have some impact upon the family. In the case of intrafamilial abuse this may be a particularly important factor, but for other women who have had other experiences this may not be the case. Once established the eating disorder leads to a change in the nature of other problems and may serve to make these seem less important. Hence it is possible to hypothesize that unwanted sexual experience may contribute to the development of an eating disorder in some extremely important way without being the sole factor accounting for it.

Figure 3:

A FINAL MODEL TO EXPLAIN RELATIONSHIPS BETWEEN UNWANTED SEXUAL EXPERIENCE AND EATING DISORDERS

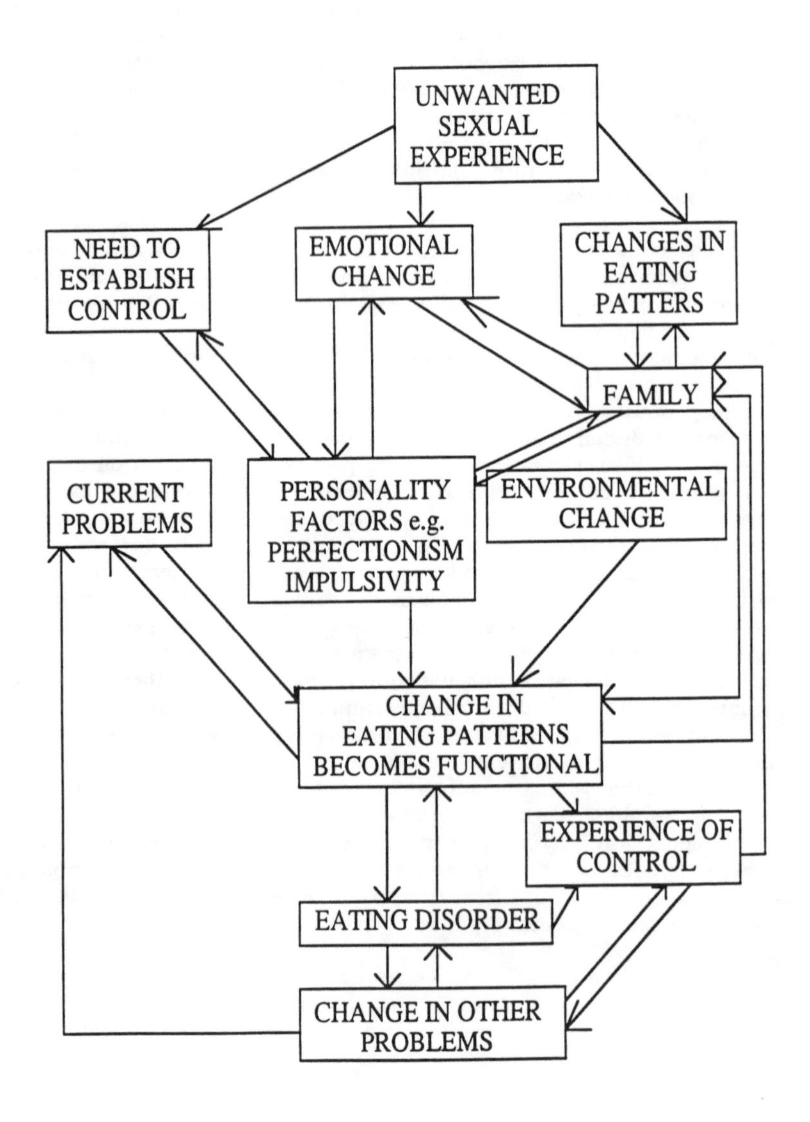

One particularly striking paper arising from a small study by Williams (1988) indicates that eating may indeed be difficult for women who have experienced abuse. Williams used the SEQ and the Eating Attitudes Test (EAT) with a group of 21 women who were attending Incest Survivors Groups. She found surprisingly high levels of scores on the EAT, the mean score for the women being 34.1, which compares with norms for female controls of 15.4. Further, she found that women who reported a larger number of unwanted experiences also had significantly higher scores on the EAT. This study is particularly interesting as it approaches the area from a different direction, and also because it serves to highlight the importance of talking to women about other areas of their life than the specific problem for which they were referred.

The women attending for therapy for eating disorders in Liverpool have found it helpful to have their sexual histories addressed and it is evident from Williams' survey of the women in Incest Survivors Groups that several could benefit from therapy for their eating difficulties. We hope very much that further patient series studies will be conducted as it is still not clear from the data to what extent links exist or how specific these may be. In particular it would appear important to conduct hypothesis-led research in order to look with a higher degree of specificity at what the nature of links between unwanted experience and eating patterns might be. At present, studies in this area address a number of different questions. One, for example, is whether rates of reporting of specific sexual experiences are higher in certain groups. Another is whether certain experiences are of particular relevance to particular groups. An overall difficulty in bringing the studies together lies in the variety of definitions and methodologies used in data collection.

It is very clear however that, as Palmer et al., (1990) conclude, women in therapy need the opportunity to talk about their sexual experiences and to be helped to explore the extent to which experiences which they have had may be affecting their current behaviour and emotional state. We have found that a questionnaire approach can be a relatively gentle and non-threatening way of approaching questions in this very difficult area and many women have said that they are very pleased to be able to talk about their experiences.

ACKNOWLEDGEMENTS: *The North American study was conducted at BASH, St. Louis. The authors would like to thank Dr. Felix Larocca, Director of BASH, and Vicki Jones, Senior Research Assistant for making available the preliminary BASH data on the SEQ.*

REFERENCES

Abraham, S. & Beumont, P.J.V. (1982) Varieties of psychosexual experience in patients with anorexia nervosa. *International Journal of Eating Disorders, 1, 10-19.*

Beckman, K.A. & Burns, G.L. (1990) Relation of sexual abuse and bulimia in college women. *International Journal of Eating Disorders, 9, 487-492.*

Calam, R.M. & Slade, P.D. (1987) Eating problems and sexual experience: some relationships. *British Review of Bulimia and Anorexia Nervosa, 2, 37-43.*

Calam, R.M. & Slade, P.D. (1989) Sexual experience and eating problems in female undergraduates. *International Journal of Eating Disorders, 8, 391-397.*

Finn, S.E., Hartman, M., Leon, G.R. & Lawson, L. (1986) Eating disorders and sexual abuse: lack of confirmation for a clinical hypothesis. *International Journal of Eating Disorders, 5, 1051-1060.*

Lacey, J.H., (1990) Incest, incestuous fantasy and indecency: A clinical catchment area study of normal-weight bulimic women. *British Journal of Psychiatry, 157, 399-403.*

Oppenheimer, R., Howells, K., Palmer, R.L. & Chaloner, D.A. (1985) Adverse sexual experiences in childhood and clinical eating disorder: a preliminary description. *Journal of Psychiatric Research, 19, 357-361.*

Palmer, R.L., Oppenheimer, R., Dignon, A., Chaloner, D.A. & Howells, K. (1990) Childhood sexual experiences with adults reported by women with eating disorders: an extended series. *British Journal of Psychiatry, 156, 699-703.*

Peters, J.J. (1976) Children who are victims of sexual assault and the psychology of offenders. *American Journal of Psychotherapy, 30, 398-421.*

Slade, P.D. (1982) Towards a functional analysis of anorexia nervosa and-bulimia nervosa. *British Journal of Clinical Psychology, 21, 67-79.*

Williams, H. (1988) *An investigation into the relationship between eating disorders and sexual abuse in a group of survivors of sexual abuse.* Unpublished undergraduate project, Department of Psychology, University of Manchester.

A SEXUAL EDUCATION PROGRAMME FOR WOMEN WITH EATING DISORDERS

Ellie van Vreckem & Walter Vandereycken

Issues of being a grown up woman with a female identity and intimate sexual relationships, as well as issues like autonomy and self-definition are often addressed in anorexia and bulimia nervosa therapy programs. In our own therapy centre we set up a sexual education group to create a stimulating and safe atmosphere in which women with eating disorders could communicate more freely about sexual themes. This chapter reports an evaluation of this group after two years.

Clinical experience and research have shown the important role of sexual problems and traumas in the development of anorexia nervosa and bulimia. Bearing this in mind we decided to experiment with a special sex-education program for women with eating disorders. It began as purely educational group sessions, which provided more information for our very young patients and created a stimulating atmosphere to communicate more freely about sexual themes. Later on the sessions shifted to group meetings with more intimate and personal expressions of bodily experiences, sexual feelings and problems. Our in-patient unit of twenty women is divided into two groups, according to the level of sexual experience, the age and the treatment phase of each person. As "warming up material" we use books and video films, which the groups are asked to read and watch one or two days before the meeting. The groups are conducted by a female psychologist and one of the female nurses.

Before we started the experiment we discussed our plans with the parents and partners of our patients. After some hesitation they were enthusiastic and collaborated actively. Some partners bought the book and read it together with our client.

The themes of the discussions are: falling in love; body experience and images; menstruation; sexuality; contraception and choice of partner. At the end of each session the group decides which one of six themes they would like to explore in the next session.

Feelings of "falling in love".

Each group member is asked to share with the group, as concretely as possible, her first "love" experiences, feelings, disappointments, memories and fantasies.

The women can talk about some nice and tender feelings, but also about their disappointments, tensions and anxieties (such as secret feelings about some teacher or classmate). Particularly the impression of 'being out of control' when falling in love is very frightening for these women. Again and again they report their two extreme attitudes, being overwhelmed by others and by their own feelings or staying distant and unattainable. This is a very important issue to deal with in our treatment, because we are convinced that finding a position in-between is essential in building up one's individuality. After such experiences of 'weakness' women often start either an even more rigorous diet or a binge period in order to punish themselves, or others, through abusing their own body.

In the younger group girls talk for the first time about their amorous feelings and are ashamed but also surprised that they can enjoy talking about them. In the group composed of older women they react more with nostalgia, realising for themselves how much they have repressed their feelings and memories.

It is surprising how often the women have forgotten their first love experiences, or even forgotten the whole period of their young adolescence. The reactions of their parents were often most denigrating, ridiculing or over-controlling. In one case for instance the parents would demand to meet the new boyfriend immediately and pass endless comments upon his character and background etc. We systematically ask about the reactions of brothers and sisters to these romantic feelings. A general attitude amongst the women is to keep all their feelings secret from their brothers. The reactions of sisters is also often remembered as extreme: either positive and supporting or extremely jealous. We wonder if this is also a feeling of their own projections of jealousy onto others or their peers. We know that this mechanism is often found in families with eating disordered women: the outside world is considered dangerous and bad and therefore all negative feelings are placed outside the family.

In the group we try to create a pleasant atmosphere. Mostly these group sessions are the most relaxing of all, we laugh a lot about the funny feelings, forgotten fantasies or clumsy reactions.

Body experiences and images

During these group sessions the 'mirror exercises' are discussed as well as memories about first body changes in puberty and reactions to it from parents, siblings and peers.

Coming from the body-orientated therapies, our mirror exercises are a focus of our treatment programme (Probs, 1990). The women carry out these 'mirror exercises' in the bathroom on the unit and they choose for themself the group member with whom they wish to do the exercises. Together they decide a time, often a quiet moment during the weekend. Dressed in a bathing suit and standing before a full size mirror they look at each other's bodies, commenting and expressing their feelings about their changing bodies. Taking into account the absence of an integrated body image, we encourage the women to focus upon different parts of their body as well as the body as a whole. Anorexics and bulimics are often fixed upon some specific part of their body.

These mirror exercises have several objectives, but the most important is the enhancement of formation of a stable, integrated, cohesive mental representation of one's own body. This is, as Krüger (1989) states, "a core body image of what is inside and what is outside and a distinct sense of boundaries between the two".

In our treatment we try to achieve this complex objective step by step and we believe that the mirror exercises constitute one of these steps. Instead of denying their real body we ask the women to clearly look at it - most of our clients report that they have not done this for months or even years. We ask them to verbalise their feelings to each other, to replace their critical eyes with loving ones and to focus upon the internal sensations and images. Anorexics and bulimics have a lack of internal evocative images of their body-self or their physiological self. They tend to rely upon external referents such as the reactions of others (Krüger 1989) or, even more often, their imagined reactions of others. By doing these exercises in pairs women can pay attention not only to their own internal work of building up body image, but also to their companions work in an intimate atmosphere. They can notice more easily the distortions and generalisations expressed by other women and thus realise their own distortions. It is also important that the atmosphere should be empathic and non-intrusive. In order to strengthen the evocation of internal body images in the art therapy sessions we ask the women to also draw the pictures of their body which they have in their own mind. Although this was developed as an evaluation method, we find it a useful a therapeutic tool.

Comments and warnings: The women do these exercises in the absence of a therapist, but this activity must not be isolated from the rest of the programme. Patients are expected to report their experiences back to the group sessions. We have noticed two major pitfalls:

1: The choice of partner. We encourage these exercise to be carried out once a week, with as many different group members as possible. When patients always select the same companion (perhaps because she is thinner) the reasons behind this must be explored in the group session.

2: Feelings of rivalry and competition. These issues are often enhanced, thus carrying out the exercise with various group members gives the women an opportunity to see all kinds of body shapes. In this way they help each other accept the differences of their bodies. Very often this is mentioned as the most positive aspect of mirror sessions.

In summary we should like to emphasise that these mirror sessions have to be considered as part of the total treatment programme and are linked firstly with the body oriented therapy and secondly with the group sessions on sexuality. Within this theme-session attention is sometimes given to the very frightening topic of masturbation. Masturbation as a way of discovering ones own body in a pleasant and loving way seems very difficult to grasp especially for the anorectic women. Women with bulimia are more familiar with it, but always seem to feel guilty and perhaps seek more painful sexual stimuli.

Menstruation

We talk about the myths concerning menstruation, the influence of social and cultural factors on the experience of menarche and about menstruation as a symbol of female sexual maturation.

All too often we find deep rooted ideas such as that women who are menstruating are unclean, contaminated, sick, to be avoided and prohibited from sexual intercourse. All too often menstruation is also associated with pain, distress, tensions and irritability. In an interesting article O'Toole (1988) describes how she works around these issues in her art therapy sessions. In order to facilitate the expression of feelings and memories she uses expressive techniques (psychodrama, rôle playing) creative writing, journal keeping and guided fantasies to re-experience first menstruations. Painful memories and negative emotions have to be accepted and shared with the group. These are counterbalanced by exploring positive associations, by creating new rituals within the group. In our groups we create a ritual celebration of the return of menses each time it happens in treatment, the woman is warmly congratulated.

Other forms of sexuality

We use guided imagery to assist women in remembering past sexual experiences for instance from early sex play with peers, homosexual feelings or encounters which were traumatic or violent. Women are asked to discuss how they felt about their bodies and their eating behaviour at that time. If incest or some traumatic experience has occurred the women most often link this to the beginning of their eating problems and try to express these feelings in the group. These group sessions are the most painful, touching and intense of all. We always work very seriously with these revelations and try to integrate them into the other regular group psychotherapy sessions (thrice weekly) and/or in separate family sessions.

We also ask our clients to examine their present lives and to recognise self-destructive patterns or relationships where they were victimised. The effects of repeated victimisation are discussed, for instance how each experience deepens their distrust of other people and increases their feelings of loneliness and isolation (see also Kearney-Cooke 1988).

It is remarkable how often group members want to speak about homosexual feelings, doubts and events, whilst being very reluctant to speak at the same time. These ideas of being 'not normal' or being homosexual appear very difficult to accept. The women often question themselves about their close friendships with other women and often need to be reassured.

Contraception

Different forms and methods of contraception are discussed and demonstrated in the group. Each group member talks about her experiences, fears and doubts. This often turns out to be the most 'medical' session of all.

Choice of partner

In these group session the participants are asked to share the rational and irrational elements in their attraction to partners.

Which physical or personal qualities are important in order to feel some attraction ? Is there a difference between sexual attraction and emotional closeness ? How does this feel for each group member ? How was it in the past and how is it now ?

Mostly the women start to talk about long forgotten events and feelings. The conscious preference for distinguished, fair haired men in contrast to desperately falling in love with the opposite - mysterious dark haired ones is very usual. To us this is an opportunity for the women to get in touch with contradictory feelings, to wake up their curiosity about their own mystery and repressed longings for adventurous love.

During these sessions a remarkable transformation within the members takes place. They become more playful, vivid and fond of teasing, as if they feel released. Other longings can also be explored, the need to be admired or to participate in the admiration of others. Why do they so often fall in love with the 'play boy' which is experienced as very threatening. The need to nurture and to be nurtured is frequently mentioned as part of the attraction of a partner.

Very often anorexic girls with possessive mothers and/or fathers unconsciously choose possessive or even jealous partners. In this context the girls enrich their discussions with questions about fear of infidelity and abandonment, but also fear of boredom, control and lack of freedom and individuality within a relationship.

Finally the image of the father and/or brother can not be avoided. How much does the partner resemble or differ from the image of the father ? Young girls as well as married women tell us about the funny, surprising or previously unnoticed details they like or dislike in their partners. We consider these group discussions as an opening of doors to a more personalised intimacy.

Conclusions

Taking into account the positive reactions of our clients and our own impressions, we are convinced that our sexual education programme stimulates the disclosure and discussion of sexual issues. Our impressions are that the women with anorexia nervosa seem to benefit more from these groups than the bulimic women, whose sexuality has to be more structured than liberated. The central theme for all of our clients is always the difficulty of handling growing intimacy with others without being overwhelmed by it. By recognising and accepting these feelings, particularly the contradictory ones, the women can begin to assert themselves in intimate relationships.

REFERENCES

Kearney-Cooke A. (1988) Group treatment of sexual abuse among women with eating disorders. *Women and Therapy, 7 5-21.*

Krüger D.W. (1989) *Body self and psychological self.* New York, Brunner Mazel.

O'Toole C. (1988) Exploring female sexuality through expressive therapies *The Arts in Psychotherapy 15, 109-117.*

Probst M., Van Coppenholle H., Vandereycken W. (1990) Evaluating the body experience of patients with eating disorders through video-confrontation. In Doll-Tepper G. et al (eds) *Adapted physical activity.* Berlin, Springer-Verlag.

Probst M., Van Coppenholle H., Vandereycken W., Meerman R. (1990) Zur evaluation der körperbild wharnehmung bei patienten mit anorexia nervosa. *Psychiatrische Praxis, 17 115-120.*

HOW IMPORTANT IS BODY IMAGE FOR NORMAL WEIGHT BUL IMPLICATIONS FOR RESEARCH AND TREATMENT

Judith Bullerwell-Ravar

Fear of becoming obese, feelings of dissatisfaction and disgust towards one's own body and desperate attempts to control weight have long been considered 'proof' of a disordered attitude towards body image in women with eating disorders. However the comparison of women with bulimia and women with no current eating problems in France throws a new light upon this belief. This chapter examines more closely the utility of the concept of 'body image distortion' and asks if clinicians should continue to isolate and 'treat' the implied aberration.

Body dissatisfaction and the bulimic syndrome

Body dissatisfaction, like self-disparagement and body image distortion, is considered to be an important factor in the psychopathology of the bulimic syndrome. Fear of fat and desperate attempts to lose weight are often quoted as proof of a body image that is as pathological as the eating disorder itself.

The links between body image and disordered eating have been demonstrated by a substantial amount of research, including comparative studies on size estimation, attitudes towards the body including dissatisaction, fear of obesity, need to control, or lose weight. (Slade, 1985; Slade, 1990)

In France the urgent request of bulimic patients - whatever their weight - when they first consult a clinician in order to stop their binge eating behaviour, is (a) not to gain weight, and (b) to lose some.

The Catch 22 aspect of the relationship between the fear of obesity and binge eating has been abundantly demonstrated. The bulimic panics at the fantasy of an "Alice in Wonderland" body which threatens to expand in an unlimited way unless control is exerted over it relentlessly, and permanently. The paradox is that the dieting and restricting behaviour tend lead to the very effects that the patient does not wish, since excessive restraint tends to trigger binge eating.

The sociocultural model of desirable slenderness can also complicate the nutritional problem. To correspond to this model, a woman often has to weigh less than her normal biological weight. In bulimic women insistance on such a goal reinforces both dieting and binge eating behaviour. The honest clinician who points out in the first session that in order to eliminate the binge eating it will probably be necessary to accept to weigh 1 or 2 kilos above the presenting ideal is likely to never see the horrified patient again!

For all the above reasons, and whatever the theoretical background of the therapist, the bulimic patient's body image is considered "disordered" since although her weight is often normal in medical terms, she panics at the idea of becoming fat. Proof of a more objective body image is usually considered to be the acceptance by the patient of her current weight, and a less obsessive desire to lose the necessary number of pounds to reach her "ideal" weight.

Therapists, faced with a bulimic patient, often adopt a treatment package, which includes food and mood monitoring, nutritional education and cognitive-behavioural methods, as well as insight-directed therapy.

Certain clinicians have wondered however, given the importance of body image for the patient, if success would not be more rapid if the accent were placed initially on the pathological aspects of body image, especially as most research shows that bulimics, once cured, are satisfied with their body image.

Problems of research and treatment concerning body image distortion

The problems are threefold, and concern:-

* *the concept itself. What exactly do we mean by body image?*
* *the measurement of body image. What exactly are we measuring?*
* *evaluation techniques, both in research and treatment.*

The concept of body image

If the practical definition of body image used in this paper is the physical and cognitive representation of the body which underlies and includes attitudes of acceptance and rejection, this is however at best a working definition.

For what body, and what body image are we talking about? The psychodynamic definitions, which emphasize the symbolic and fantasy aspects of body image, cannot be tested in a scientific research model. Other definitions, depending on the background of the researcher, may privilege the physical perception of the body and or parts of it, or on the other hand insist on subjective attitudes of acceptance and rejection. Other aspects include physiological, biological, social, psychological and cultural elements.

But it has been demonstrated that body image can be modified over time and that its limits are not fixed. Clothes can extend the image, a hat for example, or even an object held in the hand. (Schilder, 1950, Fisher, 1986). So we are dealing with a complex concept, lacking well-defined contours, not only for bulimic patients, but also for clinicans and researchers!

Thus Fisher (1986) includes in his scholarly review of research on body image, for lack of a precise scientific definition, any study which deals with "how individuals view and assign meaning to their own body" (p.1)

Measurement of body image

Researchers into the body image of bulimics have tried to study this concept in two ways, by physical measurement or by cognitive attitude. In the first case, the subject is asked to reproduce either her whole silhouette or parts of her body by means of an apparatus, more or less sophisticated, in order to measure the difference between the objective size and those indicated by the subject. Too big a difference is supposed to correspond to an erroneous evaluation on the subject's part, corresponding to body image distortion.

However, the connection has not been proved, especially as it has been shown in other research that non-bulimics and controls overestimate their size as much as bulimics. The body image problem of bulimic patients is therefore concerned with more than erroneous perception of the body.

The second type of measurement concerns the attitude towards the body, linked to the cognitive representation of what is positive or negative in the body, often measured by questionnaires.

Results of body image attitude and dissatisfaction scales are more discriminating than physical measurements. If all women wish to lose a few kilos, attitudes of anxiety and body rejection are more specifically bulimic. So this type of measure does enable us to distinguish between bulimic women and the others. However in this dichotomous distinction the connection with weight, which has its part in both types of measurement, is not very clear. However, weight is obviously an important element in how a woman perceives and feels about her body. Moreover, weight dissatisfaction has been shown to be generalised among women in industrialised countries among the female population, not only bulimics and anorexics (e.g. Rodin, Silberstein & Striegel-Moore, 1985; Birtchnell, Dolan & Lacey, 1987).

Research findings also disagree on whether bulimics and anorexics really overestimate their body size more than controls in size-estimation techniques. As to the question whether body image distortion - and indeed body image - is stable over time or not, the case in favour of stability put forward by Garfinkel et al., (1978) was generally accepted until quite recently.

Faced with these results researchers have tried both to explain the contradictory findings, and refine measurement techniques. One of the paths followed was to distinguish between cognitive elements (induced by questions such as "what do you think your size really is?" and emotional, subjective feelings (induced by questions such as "what do you feel your size is?"). Slade (1985) first suggested that different aspects of the body image were being tapped by the different techniques used and hypothesised on the one hand a relatively stable cognitive attitude to the body size and on the other a perceptual aspect that is more influenced by external factors and the emotional state of the subject.

More recently however, he has come to believe that the body image of bulimics and anorexics is "uncertain and unstable" rather than "distorted". (Slade, 1990). This position corresponds to recent research findings (Norris, 1984; Collins et al., 1987; Brinded et al., 1990). For example Norris found that bulimics and anorexics changed their judgement about their body after mirror confrontation, whereas controls did not.

Our own research, based on in-depth interviews, is that, even though perception of body size may not be stable, the attitude to the body usually is, especially when this attitude is negative, as in the case of bulimic and anorexic patients. However body image attitude corresponds to a continuum, which does not exactly reproduce that of eating disorders. It is not because a woman is unhappy with her body that she becomes bulimic.

Certain bulimics, who consider that vomiting has provided a solution to their weight problem, make a distinction between the body such as it appears on the outside, to other people, and which is satisfying provided is it controlled by vomiting, and the body perceived from the inside, which is fantasised as potentially obese.

Evaluation

Evaluation of research and therapy of body image runs up against another problem, concerning the difficulty in separating body image from other aspects of self image, and especially self esteem.

If cured bulimics have improved self esteem, self image and body image, as well as a lesser degree of depression, it is difficult to decide which factor is the most instrumental in the process, since they are linked together. To try to isolate the body image from a more global conception, such as self image, is an extremely difficult exercise.

Should clinicans "treat" their patient's body image?

Given this complexity is it possible to treat body image, and if so, how ? The following elements need to be taken into consideration:

(1) As well as the problems concerning body image already mentioned, the therapist also has to deal with the difficulty of the patient in knowing exactly what is her body image in the present.

If we can question Slade's emphasis on an "unstable" body image, to the extent that control subjects also have a modifiable body image, eating-disordered patients do indeed have an "uncertain" body image in the present. This uncertainty can moreover be explained. The anguish of bulimics is turned towards the future, where they fear to become obese, and/or towards the past, where they have often been through a period of obesity. When people say that the bulimic is a frustrated anorexic, this comes from the desire to put a maximum gap between the danger of obesity and themselves. This fear is not necessarily unfounded, many bulimics have known a past experience of obesity, which was experienced as traumatising.

More often than not, bulimic women do not live their body in the present and therefore have difficulty in representing their actual body to themselves or describing it to others. They have only a virtual image of their body in the present. It is for this reason that certain bulimics and anorexics cannot say in good faith what is their body image, and indeed need constant reassurance from outside to bolster their virtual image. However these outside indications do not reassure them for very long, and especially not further than the next food intake. They do not avoid the mirror simply because they see themselves as obese, but also because they cannot integrate what they see in it as belonging to them. Weighting scales may play the role of external censor or gauge for some bulimics, other people's scrutiny and remarks for others. However these signs, if positive, only reassure the patient for a short time, not permanently, whilst any negative reinforcement is accepted without question.

(2) Our own research, using in-depth interviews of three groups (bulimics, ex-bulimics, controls) *(see research note at end)*, indicates that, even though the desire to lose weight is a presenting symptom, this desire is shared quantitatively by non-eating-disordered women. The problem is a qualitative one, depending on a cognitive set in bulimics, who have a greater fear of obesity and a greater fear of lack of control over food, which will lead to obesity. As a consequence they have a lack of tolerance of any weight exceeding their desired weight - which corresponds not only to "desirable thinness", but also to a protective blanket against obesity.

(3) The same research also indicates that the primary problem is not one of body image perception. A sub-group of about 30% of bulimics admitted in the course of their interview that for them the problem was the danger of lack of control rather than a refusal tto acknowledge their actual body size. On the other hand, a small percentage of controls had problems with acceptance of their body.

The results of the ex-bulimics tends to indicate that the problem is one of self-acceptance and self-esteem in a larger sense that merely corporal. This result is confirmed by factor analyses of body image tests, in which the eating disorders continuum does not coincide with that of body image dissatisfaction.

The accent placed on improving body image as a means to help bulimics may therefore be less important than originally accepted by clinicians. This could explain the difficulty in separating this aspect of the problem from others such as self-esteem. In France, the body image issue seems to be important on the surface and in the discourse of bulimic patients, but in-depth interviews bring out that this aspect masks more important issues, such as self confidence and self-esteem and is more an expression of these than the cause of them.

Which methods can be most useful for body image improvement?

Given this situation, methods which are considered harsh and unpleasant by the patients - such as confrontation with a mirror - may increase their resistance.

When behavioural therapists use methods of "exposure and response prevention" it is usually in cases where the patient cannot avoid the problem in his daily life (e.g. phobias) and he or she has come to therapy in order to solve this specific problem. In the case of the bulimic, the therapeutic request is not to work on the body image, but to lose weight. Thus the "therapeutic" shock of mirror confrontation is felt to be an aggression by the bulimic patient and a very experienced therapist is needed to deal with this. However, in the case of hospitalisation, the video can be used to show that patient that she has made progress afer a certain time.

A method which enables to treat the body image in a global context is cognitive therapy, since the negative certitudes of the subject are systematically questioned, in order to help her find out what is behind them. Quite often, the bulimic, unable to defend her belief rationally, will herself discover the reason behind it (e.g. fear of failure, fear of not being good enough), thereby reinforcing her self esteem. The rational demonstration of how the body works and nutritional education can also be useful.

However the treatment of bulimia is a slow process, one of maturation. The body image at the outset is vested with a magic power, that of being able to arrange everything in the bulimic's life, provided that it corresponds to the fixed ideal. It is only when she understands that the eating disorder hides another problem, and accepts to look at what is behind it that she can begin to work on body image, in its relationship to self image and self esteem. Only then can she begin to distinguish between the fear of obesity and rejection of her body image, to examine the difficulty of living with her body in the present, and the attitude towards food and the ideal body of her family.

As to the explanation of why body image is so important to bulimics, our research findings lead us to believe that the attitude of the bulimic woman to her body depends on the attitude of her family, especially that of her mother and father, and the importance they attach to norms of slenderness in the family circle, more than on wider cultural norms. We have found that in France that most mothers of bulimics themselves have a problem with food or weight or body image, or all three.

On the other hand, comparison of our results from France with those of Fallon and Rozin (1985) in the USA tend to prove that there are cultural differences insofar as body image is concerned, and that the American female preoccupation with the body is not a universal model in Western industrialised countries.

Food, after all, has a social and cultural meaning, which enables a person to mark his/her assimilation or rejection of a cultural or a collective identity. For the bulimic, like everyone else, the family is a place of socal, relational and nutritional apprenticeship. The manipulation of food, body image and relations are thus linked together. In a bulimic family, the mother-daughter relationship often revolves around the daughter's body and eating habits, which become a place of symbolic struggle and manipulation between the two protagonists.

To isolate body image as a therapeutic objective risks to reinforce the patient in her belief that body image is indeed the most important thing in life - especially if the therapist is male.......

REFERENCES

Birtchnell, S.A., Dolan, B.M. & Lacey, H.J. (1987) Body Size Distortion in Non-eating Disordered Women, *International Journal of Eating Disorders, 6,(3) pp.385-391*

Brinded, P., Bushnell, J., McKenzie, J. & Wells, J.E. (1990) Body-Image Dostortion Revisited: Temporal Instability of Body Image Distortion in Anorexia Nervosa, *International Journal of Eating Disorders, 9,6, 695-701.*

Collins, J., Beumont, P. ,Touyz, S., Krass, J., Thompson, P. & Philips, T. (1987) Variability in Body Shape Perception in Anorexic, Bulimic, Obese, and Control Subjects *International Journal of Eating Disorders, 6, 633-638*

Fallon, A. & Rozin, P. (1985) Sex Differences in Perceptions of Desirable Body Shape, *Journal of Abnormal Psychology, 94(1), 102-105*

Fisher, S. (1986) *Development and Structure of the Body Image,* Laurence Erlbaum Associates, Hillsdale, 2 vols.

Garfinkel, P., Moldofsky, H., Garner, D., Stancer, H. & Coscina, D. (1978) Body Awareness in Anorexia Nervosa; Disturbances in body image and satiety. *Psychosomatic Medicine, 38, 327-336*

Norris, D.L. (1984) The Effects of Mirror Confrontation on Self-Estimation of Body Dimension in Anorexia Nervosa, Bulimia and Two Control Groups, *Psychological Medicine, 14, 835-842*

Rodin, J., Silberstein, L.R. & Striegel-Moore, R.H. (1985) Women and Weight: A Normative Discontent ,pp. 267-307 in Sonderegger, T.B. (Ed.): Nebraska *Symposium on Motivation: Vol.32. Psychology and Gender,* Lincoln, University of Nebraska Press.

Schilder, P. (1950) *The Image and the Appearance of the Human Body*, London, Kegan, Paul, Trench, Trubner.

Slade, P.D. (1985) A Review of Body Image Studies in Anorexia Nervosa and Bulimia Nervosa, *Journal of Psychiatric Research, 19, 255-265.*

Slade, P.D. (1990) Body Image Distortion: A Review of the Literature, *BASH Magazine, (July), 9,7, pp.196-197,222.*

RESEARCH NOTE

The author has looked at matched samples of normal-weight bulimics, ex-bulimics and non eating-disordered controls, in order to establish the extent to which attitudes towards body image differed between eating disordered and non eating-disordered French females. The results are due to be published in 1991.

Besides a semi-structured interview on self-image and body-image, the subjects filled in the E.A.T.(40-item version), and three other measures of body image: two scales concerned with body dissatisfaction, the first one dealing with global attitude, the second one with detailed parts of the body, and finally a replica of the Fallon & Rozin drawings research, using a similar protocol by two French researchers, M.Chiva and C.Fischler, called How Fat is Fat.

The interview dealt with weight and family weight histories, as well as attitudes to body image. The results indicated firstly that the desired weight of the bulimic population is close to that of the other groups, and remains within what is considered normal by the medical profession (weight index 19 to 24 for the French female population). The intergroup variation was from 19.9 to 19.3.

It was also found that global body dissatisfaction is much more discriminating (ANOVA, $p<.001$) than dissatisfaction concerning body parts ($p<.05$).

Using a series of drawings going from thin to fat (cf.Rozin, 1985), interesting results were obtained when the subjects were asked to rate themselves with reference to the figures, although the most interesting ones are trends rather than significant differences.

The majority of non-bulimics choose for themselves the figure that they had chosen as ideal for a woman, while the trend is the contrary for the bulimics. This is a very interesting result in the light of the expressed desire to lose weight in all groups. The non-bulimic group does not consider that 5 or 6 pounds above the desired weight puts them into the fat category, whereas most of the bulimics are persuaded that this is the case.

The bulimics consider themselves too fat compared to what is a desirable size for a woman and also compared to what is most attractive to men. They are however objectively normal weight.

The results of the ex-bulimics are also interesting. They no longer have a problem concerning the way they are viewed by other people, in that they no longer consider themselves too fat compared to the cultural norms, nor compared to what men appreciate. However a more personal judgement - what my real size is, and how it compares to my ideal - remain closer to those of the bulimic group than to those of the non-bulimic group. This indicates that the intimate acceptance of oneself remains vulnerable, and this may explain why so many cured bulimics relapse. An interesting finding is that, in France, two thirds of the normal-weight female population have a body image which coincides for all three measures. This corresponds more to what Rozin found for the American male population!

In fact most of the women in the global sample are either slightly happy or slightly unhappy about their body image. This may however be the result of a cultural difference between France and other countries.

THERAPEUTIC APPROACHES

WOMAN THERAPISTS FOR WOMEN PATIENTS ?

Rose Stockwell & Bridget Dolan

In our psychodynamic work with women with bulimia we find that therapy is centred more upon the conflicts and identity struggles of being an adult woman than on the symptoms of eating behaviour. Once food abuse is dealt with behaviourally the focus of our therapeutic model is on helping the woman find an identity within her society and cultural niche. We highlight five main issues which are commonly explored in therapy with bulimic women and discuss how the personal experiences of a woman therapist may make her able to offer more to the client than can a man.

"In the course of researching this book I came up against one major drawback to writing about men. ..... the majority of men do not think they have a problem. ..."

"Men" - Mary Ingham

In this chapter we contend that women therapists working with women with eating disorders have a extra resource which men do not have - being physically and emotionally a woman. We feel that many clinical teams ignore rather than exploit the gender differences between their staff members in treating women with eating disorders partly because it has not been specified in concrete terms what exactly this resource is and how it can be utilised in treatment programmes.

Our need to draw attention to this potential for improved treatments emerged from our observation that therapist's gender, until very recently, has not been an issue in academic papers on eating disorders nor in research. Many treatment outcome studies have been reported in eating disorders research, with a variety of variables considered, but no studies have specifically tried to examine the efficacy of different gender therapists nor have there been any reported trails of treatments specifically exploiting the differences between male and female therapists. In our search we could find only one experimental study that considered the issue at all. Lacey (1982) considered impact of therapist gender in group psychotherapy, his study showed that although there were no differences in behavioural outcome comparing groups with female co-therapists to those with a male and female therapist, the clients preferred to be treated by women.

We wonder if gender differences are ignored because clinicians and researchers have viewed eating disorders as a "medical" problem. As a medical problem there would be an implication that a "treatment" should be found that can be carried out by a professionally trained person regardless of their gender. It may be that this "medicalisation" of eating disorders has drawn us all into not ever questioning who is best suited to give a particular treatment or part of treatment - a man or a woman. However it also seems to us that it has been our male colleagues who have been most reluctant to take up this issue either in discussion or in research projects.

This feeling was partly reinforced by our experience at the European Council on Eating Disorders meeting when the theme of gender difference was raised. When participants were asked to discuss the question "woman therapists for women patients" in single sex groups some of the male participants were angry that they had to be in an all male group and found the topic difficult to discuss - they also felt that 45 minutes was too much time for the issue! Others retreated behind research stating that there was no evidence that women therapists had a better treatment outcome than men, thus avoiding exploration of how the gender of her therapist might effect the client and the treatment. A few men sabotaged the arrangements and joined one of the five all female groups. By contrast, women had no problem talking over this issue together and brought useful discussion material back to the meeting.

We feel that research should address the issue of gender differences directly and we suggest below some of the main areas that we feel could be the natural domain of women. We hope women therapists will find that our reflections either reinforce or supports what they already know or brings to the fore a depth of knowledge that we are convinced lies as a potential within them. We hope male therapists will find no difficulty in acknowledging their lack of experience in the female domain and will use the chapter to review their own approach to these issues and to reflect upon what they have to offer the eating disordered women they work with, in specifically male arenas.

Fundamental issues for women with eating disorders

Treatments aim to help women tolerate the thoughts, feelings, fears, and anxieties that come to mind if they stop their preoccupation with food, weight and shape. We suggest that the issues which are commonly explored and understood in a new way by the patient are:

* food and eating
* the biological experience of being a woman
* weight, shape, and feelings about different body parts
* sexuality
* different roles as a woman

We believe that the more a woman worker uses her personal comprehension of being a woman in her thinking about eating disordered women the better will be her therapeutic work. We feel that however sensitive men may be to the issues facing women this can never be an substitute for the profound personal comprehension of a woman.

We consider each of the areas listed above and raise some of the issues with which we think a woman worker will be more able, than a male worker, to help her patient. Particularly if she has reflected upon them for herself in an open and considered way and understands her own conflicts and difficulties.

In a short paper it is impossible to be comprehensive and we aware that the scenarios we suggest deal with the heterosexual woman in a partnership. Whilst this precludes the experiences of many women, we feel it reflects the majority of our clinical contact. We hope that these few examples will consistently and irritatingly raise the question "but does the gender of the helper really matter?" We feel that we should find out.

Food and eating

Despite an increasing number of men being involved in running the home, women still have far more to do with food than men. It is usually the woman who writes the shopping list, buys the food, prepares and serves most meals and deals with what remains after the meal. Each of these tasks present their own set of challenges - we will just examine shopping and leave you to think about the others. The shopping list involves money - whose money is being spent, how much can be spent; choice - who's needs are to be met, who's favourites bought, what meals are to be provided before the next shopping trip, what has run out and needs replacing, should cheap alternatives be looked for and will they be adequate substitutes, treats, low fats, low calories, cakes and biscuits or muesli bars and fruit or both; what to buy for celebrations or disappointments or whether not to use food at all for these etc. When things go wrong with any of these processes a woman can feel it reflects upon her capabilities if she is also attempting to recover from an eating disorder such tasks can be a nightmare.

As well as this 'here and now' confrontation with food there is also the history of our dealings with it from the moment we were born. There is the eating of food - quantity, experiences of likes and dislikes, differences between the male and female members of the family - and there is the social occasion of family meal times and our experiences here - differences between the expectations of males and females in helping prepare, serve and clear the meal, who talks at the table, who is present at meal times etc. Meal times are places where many families very concretely show gender differences.

The biological experience of being a woman.

A woman worker has periods, breasts, sexual organs of reproduction and knowledge of her body's changes during her monthly cycle and her mood variations. She knows the struggles of learning to enjoy herself sexually and the difficulties in matching her chosen sexuality to societal expectations. She may have faced family planning issues - the internal examination, the weighings at the clinic etc.

She knows her body has the capacity to bear a child, she may have done so or actively chosen not to, but she will have experienced some emotions regarding motherhood. The woman therapist has her own emotional experience to draw on and help her patients name feelings and learn to talk about their bodies and their bodily experiences.

Weight, shape and feelings about different body parts.

Research repeatedly informs us that women are concerned about their weight - most women, when asked, say they would like to be at least a kilogram or two lighter. Many women also have personal concerns and conflicts about their shape, about parts of their body being "wrong", about what they wear and about how they look.

Most women have first hand experience of shared changing rooms, of wondering what to wear, of wondering what to do (if anything) about hairy legs, armpits and the pubic line, of shops that never sell the clothes that suit you etc. Even those who choose not to accept social stereotypes of femininity have knowledge of the social pressures they are refusing to accept.

Sexuality

Our feelings and attitudes to our sexuality is closely linked to how we feel about our bodies and how we present ourselves not only through our clothes but our whole manner. It is closely tied up with our experiences through childhood of our own sexual development and that of parents sexual relationship and those of our brothers and sisters. These early experiences and our adult ones will effect our feelings about masturbation and sexual relationships and our capacity to enjoy our own sexuality fully. For many women with eating disorders accepting their sexuality, regardless of its orientation, is a paramount issue. Although men therapists also must deal with their own male sexuality this does not replace the intuitive and integrated sense of how women's sexuality feels for a woman.

Different roles as a woman

The woman worker is often a mother, a partner in a relationship and is always a daughter. She will, to varying extents, have understood and resolved issues about these roles. She could be a working mother juggling the demands of home with those of work. She might not have a supportive and understanding partner and may have to face conflict in the home about her role as a worker. She may be lesbian and contending with the disparity between some societal expectations of her and her own chosen sexual orientation. She may experience a partner's expectation that she be the one who deals with children unexpectedly being ill or unable to go to school and who organises the domestic side of home running. Or she might be a single woman experiencing the struggles of establishing a relationship or the demands of other family members that she look after ailing parents.

The woman worker has experience of relating to men as fathers, brothers, lovers, bosses, colleagues or friends. In each of these relationships she has had to negotiate sexuality and power and she has had to find a way to talk and express herself.

As a woman in relationship to a man there are unique situations that arise. The woman worker will probably have a variety of such experiences: - men intruding eg wolf whistles, unwanted petting or incestuous relationships; men who look down on a woman not believing that she has a mind that can function as well as or better than his; men who she can not reject and yet with whom involvement means pain; men who want to have women running around them, and many other pre-judgments of which a man would have little experience.

But the female therapist interacts with other women too, as mothers, sisters, lovers, bosses, colleagues or friends. She also has experience of how women relate to women.

Conclusion

We do not propose that a therapist has to have been through every experience of their client to be able to offer some understanding. However for women with eating disorders the conflicts and anxieties they display are often not located uniquely in the eating problem, but are related to the broad experience of being a woman within our society. We realise that our use of stereotypic women's roles runs the risk of simply creating a further stereotype of bulimic women's experiences which precludes individuality and may be distant from the detailed experiences a woman has of her own life.

We have looked at the areas where we feel women workers may be able to offer something particular to their women patients but we also believe that the male worker has his own domain.

We have given just a few examples of the experiences and conflicts of which women may have intimate knowledge and which we feel are crucial areas to address for the long term success of treatment of women with eating disorders. We suspect that some of these areas may be avoided intentionally in therapy, and that this will be determined by the gender of the worker and client. We feel that therapists of either gender should be aware of what these areas are, and we hope that our chapter will help our patients receive better treatment.

The assumption of this paper is not that women necessarily make better therapists nor that gender is the most important factor in therapy, but that there are basic differences between male and female life experiences which influence their approaches to therapy and acknowledgement of these can facilitate the therapy process (Carter, 1971). For eating disorders we must consider what therapeutic conditions are most likely to facilitate a woman's emotional growth and how we can best provide this in therapy.

REFERENCES

Carter C A. (1971) Advantages of being a woman therapist *Psychotherapy, Research and practice 8(4) 297-300.*

Ingham M. (1985) *Men: The male myth exposed* Century Publishing, London.

Lacey J.H. (1983) Bulimia nervosa, binge eating and psychogenic vomiting: A controlled treatment study and long term outcome. *British Medical Journal 286; 1609-1613.*

CAN WOMEN WITH EATING DISORDERS BENEFIT FROM A MALE THERAPIST ?

Werner Köpp

Although the majority of those who suffer with eating disorders are female the issue of whether their therapists should also be female is just beginning to be explored. This paper highlights several issues relating to therapist gender and considers the pros and cons of both male and female therapists when working with eating disordered women. It is suggested that although clients should have a choice of the gender of their therapist there are potential problems with both women and men. Ideally the therapist should be supervised by someone of the opposite gender and attention should be made to transferential and countertransferential problems.

Can women with eating disorders benefit from a male therapist ?

One could easily answer 'Yes'. However, in that doing so we would not have understood the implications of this question or the conditions under which this simple answer might be right or wrong.

If we accept Freud's recommendation (1912), the ideal therapist should be like a mirror reflecting only what the patient is showing. If a therapist could really fulfill this requirement, we would not even need to ask the above question. Gender of therapist would become immaterial as every aspect of transference would appear during a regular analysis.

There are, however, two important caveats to consider: Firstly, the therapy of patients with eating disorders usually is not a regular psychoanalysis. Secondly, more recent analytical writings on countertransference suggest that the analyst's "personal equation" and the analyst's personality structure are of great importance in the process of psychotherapy (Riemann, 1960, 1964). Thus, the "reflective capacity" of the analyst or therapist 'as a mirror' is limited because of his/her personality. Undoubtedly, the therapist's sex plays a role for both transference and counter-transference. Up till now we can only hypothesise about what role gender plays in therapy and whether it influences only the process or also the outcome of that therapy.

In recent years, feminist therapists have been suggesting fundamental changes in common types of therapy Rejecting the techniques of behavioral and analytical treatment (Burgard, 1986), they propagate a new therapeutical approach (Mies, 1978) which includes:

* *identification with the female patient,*
* *clearly evident preference for the female patient*
* *equality and equilibrium between the therapist and her female patient.*

Without using psychoanalytical terms, Scheffler (1986) emphasises that inequality between female patients and female therapists has to be analysed and made transparent as an "example of the female's inferior position which creates her dependency and her helplessness"

To exemplify feminist therapy, Burgard (1986) presents a very interesting case report of a woman (not suffering from eating disorders) in treatment with a female analyst. The female therapist is seen as supporting her patient to gain some power of her own or perhaps to "score points" off her friend. It is impressive how aspects of inequality between the therapist and her patient are taken into consideration. On the other hand, the therapist rejects any idea of the patient's masochism although the patient has lived with a boyfriend maltreating her for more than five years. Feelings of shame and guilt towards this man are not interpreted by the female therapist as intrapsychic problems but as being attributable to societal conditions hostile to women, which are experienced by the female patient and her therapist alike.

Regardless of one's own agreement with this view, we should not cut off the discussion with feminist therapists at this point. This feminist approach, considering the psycho-social aspects of the culture in which women live alongside the clients intrapsychic status, have been neglected in conventional types of therapy for many years. We should perhaps accept these aspects as being important without losing the intrapsychic perspective.

Female or male therapist ?

With regard to the question of whether female patients with eating disorders can benefit from male therapists, there is very little evidence that patients can benefit less or more with a female therapist than with a male therpist. Lacey (1985) emphasises that in his opinion the therapist's gender influences only the process of therapy rather than the final outcome. He notes that the therapist's gender seems to have a greater effect in group therapy than in individual sessions. While groups with a male and female therapists seem to concentrate more on the parental marital conflicts, the all female groups tend to concentrate on relationships with mothers in a way which the presence of a man precludes.

Various arguments for the standpoint that female therapists are preferable for female patients with eating disorders are collected below.

* Anorexia and bulimia are typical female disorders and can therefore be understood better by female therapists.

* Female therapists are less offensive and have more empathy; they handle therapeutic rules and methods in a more pragmatic way (Gürtler, 1987).

* Women have more 'female intuition'. They try to demonstrate their power rather than their weakness (Baker-Miller, 1979). Therefore, female patients need not be afraid to lose closeness in a relationship with a female therapist if they show their weakness and their power (Gürtler, 1987).

* Female therapists' reactions are more sensitive; female therapists perceive more of the feelings expressed by their patients and also show more of their own feelings than their male counterparts (Orlinsky et al., 1969).

* Given that the gender relationship in our society is one of male dominance, if a female patient is treated by a male therapist, there is a considerable danger of a second dominance within the therapeutic relationship.

There are, however, other arguments indicating that male therapists could be as good as female therapists - or perhaps even better:

* Female therapists run the risk of acting out their over-identification with their patient.

* Some female patients idealise their female therapists. This idealisation in its extreme form could lead to psychological self-destruction because the patients develop a feeling of inferiority by not being able to reach their ideal.

* A male therapist offers a better chance to work out the Oedipal conflict.

* Personal identity develops by experiencing separateness and autonomy. The opposite sex of the therapist could be conducive to this process.

* The gender relationship in our society is one of male dominance and female subordination. A therapeutic approach for the female patient is easier with a male therapist because analysis of transference and countertransference helps the patient develop realistic new coping styles.

Why choose a woman therapist ?

According to Symonds (1976), Turkel (1976) and Person (1986), female patients in urban centers tend to prefer female therapists. Person claims that we must accept that changes in values and perceptions dictate dramatically different adaptations, choices and solutions of conflicts. She suggests motives for a woman choosing a therapist of the same sex, summed up under four different headings:

* A fear that a male therapist will hold on to sexist values.

* A belief that it is too easy and tempting to fool a male therapist and thereby avoid problematic topics.

* The wish to avoid an erotic transference or countertransference.

* The explicit desire to have a strong, competent woman with whom to make a positive identification.

Based on her activity as a training analyst and supervisor, she presents a clinical vignette which illustrates that common biases - sexism included - can destroy the therapeutic process. On the other hand, regardless of gender, a therapist free of values is an impossible ideal and we must assume that the therapist's interventions and interpretations are also not value free. This must be equally true of female therapists.

Person (1986) detects a transferential pitfall for male therapists, illustrating in a case report how a female patient 'did' treatment for her therapist in the same way that she 'did' sex for her husband. Person considered this behaviour in therapy as being symbolically linked to faking orgasm. Gradually, the patient began to complain that treatment was empty despite her seeming ability to make associations, utilise interpretations and so forth.

Person also refers to Zetzel's statement (1966) that especially in short-term therapies, the female patients' wish for a role model leads to a positive transference and identification which should be regarded as a valid psychotherapeutic goal. In her opinion it is impossible to judge the impact of the therapist's gender on the therapy's result.

Meyers (1986) raises the important question whether it is not an unrealistic expectation that a female therapist could understand her female patient better. According to her, it could also be an idealisation that more and more female patients are being referred to female therapists. The idea behind is that certain issues may not have been touched with a male therapist but will come to the fore in the transference with a woman. She claims that in a complete analysis it does not matter whether the therapist is a man or a woman; but in her opinion "the therapist's gender affects sequence, intensity, and certain transference paradigms in both therapy and analysis. Certainly, the earliest transference reactions tend to be influenced by the therapist's gender, as well as by other reality factors".

Should client's have the choice of therapist's gender ?

Person supports Greenacre's standpoint (1959) "If a little discussion indicates that this is a definitely established attitude of the patients, I myself always treat it with the utmost respect and compliance, since I recognise that such a patient really would find it difficult, if not impossible, to work with an analyst of the undesired sex". For the therapy of women with eating disorders, her view of transferential and countertransferential aspects related to the gender of the therapist seems to be of great value. The participants of a workshop on the therapist's gender at the "Why Women ?" conference (in Ulm, 1990) joined this discussion with further considerations.

They stated that it is no use making generalisations about the therapist's gender in the therapy of women with eating disorders. Also, in many clients who have experienced sexual abuse the fantasies and feelings related to the therapist's gender are possibly more important than in others. A positive transference at the beginning of the therapy was considered most important. Therefore, the patient should be asked - especially in hospitals, where the patient does not always have the choice of her therapist - whether the therapist's gender is of any importance for her.

It was stated that empathy is necessary for any type of therapy with women who have eating disorders. On the other hand, over empathising could be a pitfall which leads to a situation where there is no room for conflict. The patient's ability to disagree with her therapist was considered a very important step forward in the course of therapy.

Transferential and countertransferential problems may occur in therapies with both male and female therapists. As an ideal neutral attitude of the therapist is not possible, some remarkable claims not yet discussed in the literature were made:-

* *No therapist should treat any woman with eating disorders without supervision.*

* *If the therapist is male, the main supervising person should be female (and vice versa).*

* *If the therapy of a woman with eating disorders seems to become impossible in the patient's view because of gender related transferential problems, a change of the therapist should be considered.*

Any consideration in such a situation should concentrate upon the question "what enables the patient to start or to continue the therapy ?" In this context, issues of defense mechanisms and resistance are of secondary importance to the practical issue of keeping the client engaged in therapy.

REFERENCES:

Baker-Miller, J. (1976) *Toward a new psychology of woman.* Beacon, Boston. German trans: *Die Stärke weiblicher Schwäche.* Fischer, Frankfurt/Main (1979)

Burgard R. (1986) Warum brauchen wir feministische Therapie ? *Beiträge zur feministischen Theorie und Praxis, 9,(17) 41-52*

Freud S. (1912) Ratschläge für den Arzt bei der psychoanalytischen Behandlung *Gesammelte Werke, 8,* Fischer, Frankfurt/Main (1973), 384

Greenacre P. (1959) Certain technical problems in the transference relationship. *Journal of American Psychoanalytic Association. 7, 484-502*

Gürtler H. (1987) Arbeiten Therapeutinnen anders ? Der Einfluß des Geschlechts auf das therapeutische Verhalten. In: Rommelspacher P. (Ed.): *Weibliche Beziehungsmuster.* Campus, Frankfurt/Main

Heimann P. (1969) Gedanken zum Erkenntnisprozeß des Psychoanalytikers. *Psyche 23, 1, 2-24*

Kemper W. (1953) Die Gegenübertragung. *Psyche 7, 10, 593-626*

Lacey JH. (1985) Time-limited individual and group treatment for bulimia. In: Garner DM and Garfinkel (Ed.): *Handbook of Psychotherapy for Anorexia and Bulimia.* Guilford, New York-London

Meyers HC.(1986) Analytic work by and with women. The complexity and the challenge. In: Meyers HC (Ed.): *Between analyst and patient. Dimensions in countertransference and transference.* The Analytic Press, Hillsdale/New Jersey.

Mies M. (1978) Methodische Postulate zur Frauenforschung (cited by Burgard)

Orlinsky DE, Howard KI, Hill JA. (1969) The therapist's feelings in the psychotherapeutic process. *Journal of Clinical Psychology, 25, 83-93*

Person ES. 91986) Women in therapy: therapist gender as a variable. In: Meyers HC (op.cit.)

Racker H. *Estudios sobre tecnica psicoanalitica.* (1959). German version: *Übertragung und Gegenübertragung. Studien zur psychoanalytischen Technik.* Reinhardt, München-Basel (1982)

Riemann F. (1960) Bedeutung und Handhabung der Gegenübertragung.*Zeit. für Psychosomatische Medicin, 6, 2, 123-132*

Riemann F. (1964) Die Struktur des Analytikers und ihr Einfluß auf den Behandlungsverlauf. In: Salzmann L, Schwidder W, Westerman Holstijn AJ (Ed.). *Fortschritte der Psychoanalyse Bd. 1,* Hogrefe, Göttingen.

Scheffler S. (1986) Feministische Therapie. *Beiträge zur feministischen Theorie und Praxis, 9, 17, 25-40*

Symonds A.(1976) Neurotic dependency in successful women. (cited by Person)

Turkel AR. (1976) The impact of feminism on the practice of a woman analyst (cited by Person)

Zetzel ER. (1970) The doctor-patient relationship in psychiatry. (cited by Person).

SELF-HELP GROUPS FOR WOMEN WITH BULIMIA NERVOSA.

Jennifer Munro & Malcolm Laing

The development of a self-help group for women suffering from bulimia nervosa in Edinburgh is described. This self-help group arose when clients participating in a therapist-led group treatment programme for bulimia nervosa expressed a need for further support. The self-help group was developed in conjunction with the clinic's own long-term follow-up groups. The aim of the self-help group is to encourage all clients who have completed the psychoeducational group treatment to continue to tackle their bulimic symptoms whilst also learning to develop a more satisfactory supportive relationship within a group environment. This self-help group is therefore exclusive to clients who have received professional treatment in the clinic. This paper discusses our experiences of the value and the difficulties in setting- up such a group for women suffering from bulimia nervosa.

The value of self-help treatment for bulimia nervosa has become more apparent as the number of sufferers appears to be on the increase in the Western World. The few papers on self-help suggest that it has an important role in providing support to women with eating disorders who have not responded to medical or psychiatric treatment or who do not wish to approach professional help regardless of the severity of their problem, (Deeble et al., 1990; Malenbaum et al., 1988). In addition to this they can provide an excellent supportive system for the relatives and friends of an eating disorder sufferer. However, it could be argued that women who have responded positively to treatment may also benefit from community based self-help groups. This is particularly the case in busy health service settings where facilities for long term support are often not available.

It is well recognised that a follow-up treatment period of at least twelve months is required for permanent changes to be made (Oesterheld, 1987; Hsu, 1986). The symptoms of bulimia nervosa are likely to re-occur in times of stress. In dealing with such a chronic fluctuating disorder it is important to foresee the limitations of therapy. A client may do extremely well within the safety of a therapeutic relationship but this does not necessarily protect her from future difficulties. We have found in our experiences that a recurrence of the symptoms is often incorrectly attributed to "relapse" and therefore "failure".

One way of assisting women to continue to tackle their bulimia after treatment is to encourage them to continue to support each other outside the clinic. This may be a particularly effective strategy in group treatment where relationships between bulimia sufferers have already been established. As yet the value of self-help as a progression from group therapy has not been fully examined.

This article explores thie role of self-help groups after formal therapy based on our own experiences of encouraging women from our clinic in Edinburgh to continue to meet outside the therapy setting.

Our self-help group has evolved in adjunct to a psycho-educational group treatment. The group is our main treatment for bulimia nervosa because the referral rate for bulimia nervosa to our service has doubled in the space of one year. To date we have run twelve groups which have been exclusively for female patients. We do not treat enough male patients with this disorder to allow for a satisfactory male/female balance in each group.

The facility is known as the "Bulimia First Aid Group" as the remit is to teach alternative coping strategies to replace binge eating and vomiting. The main emphasis is on self-help and mutual support. The group is closed and offers a two year package with three phases. The initial intensive phase comprises of twelve weekly sessions, phase two, involves follow-up groups one month after the intensive phase and then at three monthly intervals. The third phase is the use of self-help in the community. All women who complete the package are encouraged to meet in their own time and maintain an active support group.

This third phase was initiated by some of the women who had completed the first 12 week phase. They expressed a need to continue to tackle their symptoms whilst exploring some of the broader issues around their eating disorder. They were enthusiastic about setting up a self-help group for these reasons. The therapists felt that, because of the ethos of the group treatment, this could be a positive therapeutic step. We felt that the transition into self-help could be well supported by the phase two follow-up groups and hopefully encourage a higher attendance at these important therapy follow-ups.

The aims of the self-help group are:-

* *As a Forward Progression from Therapist-Led Groups*
* *To Encourage Continued Mutual Support*
* *To Allow for Exploration of Broader Issues Around Eating Disorders*

We provided practical guidance and support. Initially we helped the women arrange to meet in a local town-hall but numbers were too small to reach the cost of this. The group meetings have since been held in members' houses.

We run therapy groups consecutively in the centre. The two women who initiated the self-help were invited to come along to the next group and describe their self-help proposal near the end of the 12 week phase. In this way the patients currently attending the therapy group were encouraged to move on to community based self-help. We have recently tried to aid this by allowing self-help meetings to be held in the clinic when a therapy group is at this transition stage.

The group has been initiated for one year now and has not run without problems. The main aims of this paper are to address some of the areas of difficulty Obviously there are always problems in organising self-help groups in any field so we will consider issues that may be of particular relevance to bulimia nervosa and these are listed below:

* *Losing the Support of the Therapist*
* *The Transition From Clinic to Community*
* *Sharing Responsibility for the Running of the Group*
* *Having Enough Motivation Outlying Realistic Expectations & Goals*
* *Coping with Group Dynamics*

Losing the Support of the Therapist

After establishing a relationship in therapy it is then important for the client and therapist to work together towards termination of treatment. This poses a problem in a group setting where there is less time to spend addressing individual's personal feelings about leaving intensive therapy. Although it is fully stressed in our group treatment that the service provides a long follow-up period, some of the group members may feel that they are only beginning recovery by the end of the twelve week phase. In this case they feel that their requirements for more input and support may not be met by self-help.

It is tempting for a therapist at this stage to respond to the feelings of "not giving enough" by adding in extra appointments but this does not encourage the bulimic woman to discover that she is responsible for her own progress and recovery. The self-help group can, given the chance, provide an opportunity for discovering autonomy and independence in overcoming bulimia nervosa.

Transition from Clinic to Community

We often find that some bulimic women who have requested professional help may find it easier to accept their symptoms in an environment that is clearly separate from every-day life.

Part of recovery involves testing out treatment strategies beyond the doors of the clinic. For sufferers of bulimia nervosa this can be a very uncomfortable experience. A bulimic woman may be perceived as coping very well externally. She may hold a good job, be involved in social and sexual relationships, thus leaving friends and family with no concept of the internal chaos that she suffers.

The secrecy of the disorder allows her to defend herself; by coping externally she can avoid the self-confrontation that is required for a complete recovery. "Taking the bulimia into the community" without its defences is threatening. Many women describe a much higher degree of anxiety attending a self-help group than a clinic. It appears that to be able to address her bulimia in a more natural setting she must be motivated and willing to change.

Sharing Responsibility

Many bulimic women describe feeling that they ought to be able to cope and take on responsibility for many things in their lives. They feel it is important to have the approval of others and that shunning responsibility is attributed as a personal failure.

This can lead to difficulties if responsibility for the running of a group is not shared equally and the issues around responsibility are not explored in honesty. The woman taking this on may herself have many unmet needs, find it hard to let go of the responsible role and would in such a case be better in a less demanding role where she could learn to express her needs and fears.

This can leave others feeling redundant or angry that they are not given the opportunity to share the work. If group leaders are selected they must be sure that they are able to cope with the responsibility, rejection, criticism and the delegation required in this role.

We feel that it is important for bulimic women to be aware of the difficulties they can experience in taking or sharing responsibility in a self-help group. Noble (1987) suggests that responsibility is rotated equally around the women in her description of a compulsive eaters self-help group, this may be an effective strategy.

Expectations and Goals

One of the problems we experience in our group treatment is that high expectations for recovery are created. This is probably due to the fact that both therapists and clients have difficulty in accepting that therapy cannot produce lasting permanent changes without a great deal of motivation from the sufferer herself over a long period of time. We find ourselves questioning our treatment strategies for bulimia nervosa far more than for other psychiatric disorders. This is probably because we find it hard to accept the difficulties in treating bulimia successfully and permanently. There is often a strong feeling from our clients of wanting to be "cured" yet the reality is that in many cases recovery involves a lot of self-evaluation and can cause extreme distress.

We therefore advise that the expectations of a self-help group be drawn out carefully at the start, and several questions addressed such as;

* *Is the group for support only regardless of whether group members want to change or not?*
* *Are there treatment goals and if so is everyone going to have the same goals?*
* *If not will some members become isolated from others?*
* *Is there enough flexibility within the group to allow members to move at their own speed and not feel out-of control?*
* *How structured is the group going to be? Will there be themes for each meeting or will it be open unstructured discussion?*

It is not possible for us to really make recommendations on these issues as there is little objective evidence for what makes an effective group. We feel that there may be more difficulty in setting goals after all the women have been through therapy. We have found that tension can arise if some group members have unrealistic expectations of the self-help replacing therapy. This is possibly one of the drawbacks to having an exclusive group of women who have all shared the same therapeutic experience. It has to be clarified that the group is for mutual and shared support for women who wish to help themselves regardless of any differences in their symptomatology.

There is a susceptibility for eating disorders groups to become dominated by discussions about foods, diets and symptom swapping. The group should be encouraged to ensure that such discussions do not avoid underlying issues. This is not an easy task for bulimic women who often feel "safer" talking to each other at this more superficial level for fear of exposing "what they are really like"

Treatment Response

In our group each woman's response to treatment is probably highly relevant to the motivation she has towards self-help.

Women who are symptom free after the first phase sometimes reject the opportunity to use the self-help group. This is possibly due to their need to leave their eating disorder behind and not look further into their problems. These women should be reminded that their symptoms may recur and that support can help them overcome future difficulties without them feeling that they have "failed" and are "back to where they started" support may be necessary in the future and that a relapse of their symptoms does not label them as a" failure".

Women who have made some progress but are still troubled with symptoms or who feel they have unresolved issues to address seem to be most likely to move forward into self-help. It is important for them to acknowledge the feelings of loss they may experience when they no longer receive intensive psychotherapy.

A proportion of women who make no progress or who become worse through therapy tend to not attend the self-help phase. Again it is helpful for them to realise that recovery from bulimia may be a slow and painful process and they may find that they will be able to use their experiences of therapy when they feel able to start to change. The self-help group should be able to provide support for these women without labelling them as treatment failures.

Coping With Group Dynamics

We predicted that without therapists to recognise and guide feelings created within the group, the women may feel uneasy about addressing any tensions or difficulties that arise. However even within the short space of the intensive treatment phase we find that many important issues are confronted.

This experience allows the group to address problems such as jealousy, and control surprisingly quickly. The anxieties about not coping with group dynamics are often far worse that reality! It is likely to be helpful for the group to have some time to consider the departure of a group member as well as the arrival of a someone new. When group members attend for the first time it seems to be easier for them to attend together.

Our self-help group is continuing to develop along with our therapy groups. We feel that, although the success of this group is limited at present, it is a valuable step - forward from therapy that would otherwise not be available for the women who feel the benefits of it.

REFERENCES

Deeble E., Crisp A., Lacey JH. & Bhat A. (1990) A Comparison between Women Seeking Self-Help and Psychiatric Treatment in Anorexia Nervosa and Bulimia. *British Journal of Medical Psychology, 63,65-72.*

Hsu G. & Holder D. (1986) Bulimia Nervosa, Treatment and Short Term Outcome. *Psychological Medicine, 16,65-70.*

Malenbaum R., Herzog D., Gisenthal S. & Wyshak G. (1988) Overeaters Anonymous, Impact on Bulimia. *International Journal of Eating Disorders, 7, 139-145.*

Noble K. (1987) Self-Help Groups: The agony and the Ecstasy, in Lawrence M. *Fed Up and Hungry, 115-135,* Women's Press.

Oesterheld J., McKenna M. & Gould N. (1987) Group Psychotherapy of Bulimia : A Critical Review. *International Journal of Group Psychotherapy, 37 (2) 163-185.*

WHAT ABOUT THE MEN ?

SELF-HELP GROUPS FOR PEOPLE WITH EATING DISORD
IS THERE A PLACE FOR MEN ?

Pat Hartley

This article looks at some of the issues surrounding the involvement of men in self-help groups for eating disordered patients, their relatives and friends. There is tentative evidence that the incidence of eating disorders in men is increasing. To deny access to male patients would be to discriminate unfairly against them. As support is offered to family and friends it would be equally unfair to exclude the male subgroup. Accepting males into a self-help group may increase the men's sensitivity to women's needs. It may also modify the female perception of male issues. Women are under some pressure to conform to society's expectations, but men may also have difficulty in meeting the high demands of today's competitive world. The changing role of women in society may lead the less secure male to question his own identity. The self-help group provides a safe forum for such issues to be explored. The presence of men in a self-help group may enable women to deal more confidently with men, within and outside the group. Many women clients are treated by male clinicians, male therapists may increase their own understanding of women's life experience by attending the groups. The aims of the self-help group include increasing awareness and understanding of eating disorders and it seems imperative that the knowledge and information members possess should be available to all, regardless of gender.

The acknowledgement by William Gull (1874) of the occasional occurrence in men, led to the term 'anorexia nervosa' being used in preference to 'anorexia hysteria' as hysteria was considered a uniquely female condition. More recent studies disclose an approximate ratio of eighteen female to one male sufferer. To deny access to self-help and support would be to discriminate unfairly against the male patient. Further, as there are relatively few cases in men, separate self-help groups are simply not feasible. Studies of younger patients with anorexia nervosa have shown a higher incidence in males than would be expected from the adult prevalence figures. (Fossen, Knibbs, Bryant-Waugh & Lask, 1986, Jacobs and Isaacs, 1986). Several useful studies have compared male and female patients, finding similar clinical features in both groups. (Vandereycken and Van den Broncke, 1984).

Although many interesting theoretical explanations have been postulated for the higher incidence of eating disorders in women, as yet none has been conclusive. It has been maintained that women are prey to greater cultural and societal pressures than men. Such pressures tend to find powerful expression through the media and focus not simply on the traditional role of women as carers and support systems but also on the ideal shape, size and appearance to which such carers should aspire. These messages frequently contain conflicting demands. A detailed discussion of these issues is beyond the scope of this paper but one media image is that the perfect wife must ensure that she provides only 'safe' foods for her husband who must be mindful of his cholesterol levels. Equally, as a mother, she must answer to her children's frequent requests for "fast food". At the same time, however, if she is to maintain her relationship with her partner and the admiration of her children, she must not eat any of these foods herself.

The media exploit men too within this process as even male products are frequently promoted through the inclusion of the ideal female with the ideal car which successful men are meant to possess. The notion that such pressures are confined to women may therefore be refuted by some men. In recent years expectations imposed on men have changed in focus. There is still great emphasis on strength and power in the male. Such strength is displayed in physical terms in films for example - the Rambo series - and the 'macho' image beloved by body-builders. Physical fitness in males can be achieved by exercise and diet. In addition, contemporary philosophy requires high levels of success in career terms, with, it may be suggested, little regard for success in personal relationships. Modern man, however, is also encouraged to find his mate. This final goal is to be sought by the same process by which all goals may be achieved - strength and power. There is much emphasis on the male as financial provider for his family but little in the way of the satisfier of their emotional needs. Women, responding to the media 'ideal' male, but at some level recognising their own emotional needs, would perhaps prefer some kind of 'combination model'. Such confusion may lead to internal conflict in both women and men. The more sensitive man, in the face of this conflict, may question his role in society and also his personal identity.

In the case of male patients some useful information about family relationships has been provided. Sreenivasan (1978) described a family background typical of his sample of male anorexics. "The mothers, oversensitive and insecure, were partnered by men who project the cultural image of masculinity, including over-indulgence in alcohol. The parents as a whole were over-weight, but obesity was more noticeable in the fathers. The patients were relatively immature and obsessional, two being markedly obsessional. The families were skewed, with marital difficulties and overt hostility between fathers and patients on the one hand, and over-dependence between the mothers and patients on the other. The onset of severe calorie restriction followed real or feared obesity." Perhaps men view eating disorders as one way of rebelling against society's image of the ideal male.

Of the five men seen within the Salford project, two had failed aspirations to a career in professional football, one is a policeman with fifteen years experience, one is a commercial artist and the fifth is unemployed. All describe very poor relationships with their fathers who in the case of those in employment, had chosen their careers for them. These fathers had reacted very negatively to both failure in the footballers and expressed dissatisfaction with his occupational role by the policeman. Interestingly, the artist and the unemployed patient had long ago severed all connection with their fathers and had made more progress towards recovery than the other three who were still very much involved with their original families, though all were married with children of their own.

One of the functions of the self-help group is to increase levels of understanding about eating disorders. As self-help groups embrace families and friends as well as sufferers, it would be inappropriate to exclude fathers, partners, brothers or friends. To do so would in fact impoverish the experience of female group members.

Much has been written about poor communication in eating disordered families. By providing a non-threatening environment, self-help groups can facilitate communication, providing a useful forum where women can increase the male's understanding of female needs but conversely gain more insight into the needs of men. Male partners, hearing from other women about the way they experience life in general and relationships in particular, may thus be able to understand and accept similar sentiments when expressed by their own female friends or partners. In this way change may be possible.

Many women attending self-help groups are receiving treatment from male clinicians. The presence of men in the self-help group may lead to a greater sense of trust in the male therapist and greater confidence in their own ability to deal with relationships with males, inside and outside the group. Conversely, male therapists may have much to learn from attending the self-help group where women feel free to express themselves honestly.

The precise incidence of sexual abuse in the history of the eating disordered client is as yet unknown. It is sufficiently well-documented to be seen as a serious factor in many cases. The safety of the self-help group where individuals are free to be themselves, would enable women who have been abused to develop some sense of trust in relationships with men in a setting where sexuality is not a predominant issue.

Where families attend self-help group meetings some discussion may focus on the role of parents. It is believed that parents act as role models for their offspring. In normal circumstances, children, even as adults, rarely gain the opportunity to comment on the type of parenting they receive. The self-help groups can provide this opportunity, allowing sons and daughters to explain how they perceive their own needs, which may or may not be met by parents. Equally, both mothers and fathers may express to clients the difficulties they experience as parents.

Many of those at self-help groups are from single-parent families. Where the single parents are mothers, the presence of fathers in the group extends the experience of the young person growing up in a predominantly female household. In addition, at the Salford group there are several fathers who come alone. Neither the sufferers nor their mothers have attended throughout a three-year period. In these cases, the presence of these men is crucial - not only for their daughters' sake but also for those female sufferers who may not personally have experienced such a sensitive and caring attitude in their own male contacts.

In conclusion, the aims of the self-help group include increasing awareness and understanding of eating disorders. The knowledge and expertise contributed by sufferers, families, friends and health professionals should be available to all, regardless of gender.

REFERENCES

Fossen A., Knibbs J., Bryant-Waugh R. & Lask B. (1986) Early onset anorexia nervosa. *Archives of Diseases in Childhood, 62, 114-18.*

Gull W.W. (1874) Anorexia nervosa (apepsia hysteria, anorexia hysteria). *Transactions of the Clinical Society, London, 7, 22-8.*

Jacobs B.W. & Isaacs S. (1986). Pre-pubertal anorexia nervosa: a retrospective controlled study. *Journal of Child Psychology and Psychiatry, 27, 237-50.*

Sreenivasan U. (1978) Anorexia nervosa in boys. *Canadian Psychiatric Association Journal, 23, 159-62.*

Vandereycken W. & Van den Broncke S. (1984). Anorexia nervosa in males. *Acta Psychiatrica Scandinavica, 70, 447-54.*

ANOREXIA NERVOSA IN BOYS

Rachel Bryant-Waugh

Previous studies have suggested that amongst those suffering from eating disorders, the male-female ratio is much higher in pre-pubertal and pubertal children than in adolescents and young adults. This paper addresses this issue and poses three main questions:

* **Do boys present with the same eating disorders as girls ?**

* **How can the higher ratio of males be explained ?**

* **Are boys harder to treat ?**

It will be proposed that the role of gender may be less central to the development of eating disorders in children than in older age groups. Case histories of boys with anorexia nervosa will be used as illustrations.

In our own retrospective study of the presentation, course and outcome of anorexia nervosa in children aged between 8 and 14 years (Fosson et al., 1987; Bryant-Waugh et al., 1988) we found an unusually high number of males. Thirteen (or 27%) of the 48 children included in our study were boys. This was of great interest to us, as this figure is very high compared to estimates of the percentage of males in older age at onset patients (that is, adolescents and young adults). The ratio of males to females is usually placed somewhere between 1 to 10 (9%) and 1 to 20 (5%) (Vandereycken & Van de Broucke, 1984; Hall et al., 1985). However, Jacobs & Isaacs (1986) found a similarly high percentage of males in their study: 6 (or 30%) of their pre-pubertal anorexics were male. Taken together with anecdotal evidence and a consistently high percentage of young boys referred to our eating disorders clinic this makes us believe that in children, males present for treatment at a higher ratio to females than in older patients.

Three questions detailed above arise from this, and will be dealt with briefly in turn.

Do boys present with the same eating disorders as girls?

It is generally agreed that anorexia nervosa can and does occur in men (Crisp and Burns 1983). There are some obvious sex related differences in presentation, such as ammenorrhea being the manifestation of endocrine disturbance in females, but on the whole there appears to be little difference between the sexes in terms of the physical features of the disorder (Sterling &

Segal, 1985) - weight loss, emaciation, hormonal changes and starvation related symptoms are found in both males and females. In children, the clinical picture is also similar.

It is more difficult to be certain that the psychopathological features of the disorder are the same in both sexes. Again, it is generally agreed that both display the characteristic fear of fatness, refusal to maintain a normal weight, and rigidity in thinking. These features are also found in children of both sexes.

Matthew was an 8 year old pre-pubertal boy with twelve month history of eating problems involving reduction in food intake. This had become acute over the month prior to referral. On examination he was found to be 80% of the appropriate weight for his height, he had not previously been overweight. He engaged in excessive exercising and had begun salivating to avoid excess fluid. He was not apparently vomiting, binge eating or abusing laxatives at presentation. His expressed reason for food refusal was that he wanted to be a runner and so 'must not get fat'. He displayed a marked fear of fatness and was depressed. He also considered himself fat even though he was clearly under weight. Over the past few months he had taken an increasing interest in cooking, and liked to help his mother in the kitchen.

It has been suggested that male patients tend to be homosexual or show disturbed gender identity development (Fichter & Daser, 1987) - in particular that males with atypical gender role behaviours have an increased risk for developing eating disorders. This view is by no means universally held - for example, Crisp and his colleagues claim that there is no reason to believe that male anorectics have a disturbed gender identity (Crisp et al., 1986). Clearly, this is a complex issue, and one that involves information that is very difficult to obtain reliably and objectively. In children, we do not consider this to be a particularly useful theory.

In conclusion, it is our contention that boys and girls presenting with anorexia nervosa do suffer from the same disorder and that physical and psychopathological features are essentially similar in both sexes. All the boys in our retrospective study mentioned earlier, fulfilled our own diagnostic criteria for anorexia nervosa (Fosson et al., 1987) as well as DSM III criteria (APA 1980). However, it is of interest to note that over the past few years we have been seeing a wider range of eating disorders in the boys attending our clinic - a number present with what Higgs et al., (1989) have called "food avoidance emotional disorder", others present with eating problems stemming from severe obsessive-compulsive disorder, or highly selective eating behaviours (distinct from anorexia nervosa).

How can the higher ratio of males be explained ?

In our own thinking and clinical work with children with anorexia nervosa at Great Ormond Street, we have found Slade's (1982) model for understanding the emergence and maintenance of eating disorders extremely helpful. He views anorexia nervosa as an "attempted adaptive strategy ... given the major setting conditions of the individual's current life situation" (Slade 1982). The diagram represents a simplification of his aetiological model and illustrates three main areas of relevance in understanding the development of the eating disorder: individual vulnerability, background conditions and triggering factors.

Figure 1:

SIMPLIFIED AETIOLOGICAL MODEL FOR ANOREXIA NERVOSA

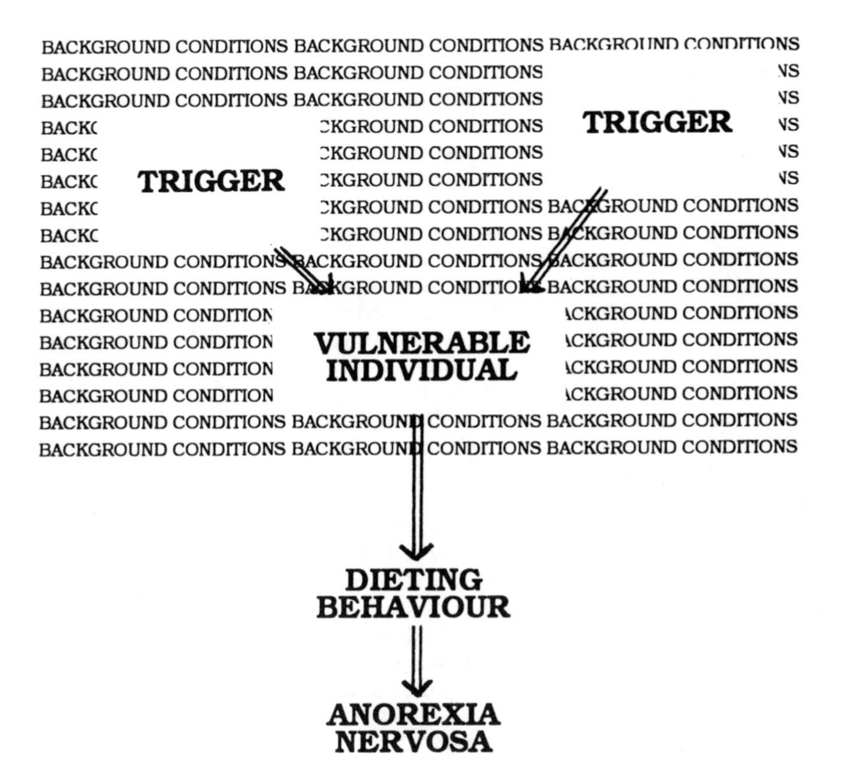

Given that the end point - the eating disorder - is essentially similar in individuals of all ages, which we believe to be the case, we need to look at how age may relate to the relevant background conditions, individual vulnerability and triggering factors. It is our belief that some of the background and precipitating factors that may play a role in the development of eating disorders in children are less sex specific that in older individuals, and this is an important reason why the sex imbalance, although still present in children, is less marked. The following case history may help to illustrate this.

Case History - Jonathan T

Jonathan was a thirteen year old boy referred to the eating disorders clinic from the renal ward of the Hospital. He was given a diagnosis of anorexia nervosa.

Family Situation: Jonathan was the elder of two boys, both of whom lived at home with their mother (who was slightly overweight). Their father, who had died two years previously, had asthma but continued to smoke and drink heavily. He had been very devoted to his work and had often not been at home. The parents' marriage was described by Mrs. T as "awful", and the eventual separation and divorce had been very stormy. After the separation, the boys went to their father most weekends. Mrs. T felt that this had been very stressful for them, and that at times they had been afraid of their father. Two years prior to admission, Jonathan had been unwell and did not go with his brother, Mark to his father's. In the night, Mr. T became unwell and woke Mark trying to telephone for an ambulance. Mark called one and accompanied his father to the hospital. Mrs. T was called and informed that her husband had died. She sent the lodger to collect Mark while she stayed with Jonathan (who was ill). Later she told both boys that their father had died.

Family Interaction: The T family were a very articulate, close family. Mrs. T was in control, but asked the boys their opinion. She was at times somewhat overprotective and there was some denial of family conflict. Mark appeared to have mourned his father's death, was able to talk openly about this and admit to negative feelings. Jonathan was more guarded; he could not allow negative feelings, avoided confrontations and was always keen to please.

Developmental and Medical History: Jonathan was born following two miscarriages. Mrs. T had been very anxious throughout the pregnancy. The birth was described as "horrendous", with Jonathan being induced against his mother's wishes. He was a normal birth weight, and a healthy baby who fed well. He had a normal development, was contented and easy to comfort. There was no history of emotional or behavioural problems with the exception of some slightly obsessional fads. There was no history of feeding difficulties. Jonathan was described as a rather solitary child.

There was nothing of apparent relevance to his medical history: he was reported to suffer from hay fever in the summer and to occasionally complain of headaches. He had no previous treatment for an eating disorder, and had never been overweight.

History of Presenting Problem: Jonathan had always had a tendency to become obsessed with certain interests. This had started at the age of 2 with the Wombles (bear-like creatures featured on a children's television series), and had progressed through Batman, Adam Ant (a pop figure), electronic music, and finally food and health. His mother recognised a pattern in these fads, which had always previously passed with time. However, the preoccupation with food and health, which had started three months prior to admission to the renal ward, had intensified over the last two months with increasing physical deterioration. Jonathan would check foods for additives, and refuse anything he thought might be harmful. Jonathan counted his calorie intake meticulously, not allowing his daily intake to go above 300 kcal. Each morning he rose at 6.30am to run one mile before going to school, and each evening he ran a further two miles. When he began to panic about missing his morning run his mother sought medical advice. She had become worried about his survival and about whether he might be causing himself permanent physical damage.

In the two weeks prior to admission, Jonathan had been in the middle of revision and exams. He and his mother had negotiated a truce for this period, which involved his mother not mentioning food to him. Admission was finally precipitated by kidney failure due to severe weight loss.

Physical and mental state examination on admission: On admission, he was extremely thin with evidence of generalised muscle wasting. His weight had dropped to 72% of the desired weight for his height and he was in the second of the five stages of pubertal development.

There was no evidence of overt depression, vomiting, laxative abuse or binge eating, although excessive exercising, fear of fatness and distortion of body image were all deemed to be present. Jonathan's main expressed reason for food refusal was the need to "avoid too much fat in the heart and blood". A diagnosis of anorexia nervosa was confirmed.

If we consider the possible precipitating factors in Johnathan's case we can propose the following as probably being relevant:

* death of father
* parental separation and marital tensions
* family dieting and weight problems (uncle and mother)
* exam time

Clearly, there may be others. However, this case illustrates well some of the themes we see recurring regularly in children with anorexia nervosa, few of which are particularly sex specific. In Matthew's case mentioned earlier, potential precipitating factors included a family move, a change in school class (resulting in the loss of friends), and his mother commencing an oligoantigenic diet for medical reasons. In Nicholas, a 12 year old boy with anorexia nervosa, relevant factors were considered to be the divorce of an uncle and aunt (Nicholas was close to the uncle who then left the area) and the death of a friend's father with Nicholas subsequently becoming concerned about his own father's health.

It is interesting to note that in boys, the refusal of food and expressed wish not to become fat is often closely linked with health and fitness, as with Jonathan, rather than with notions of an ideal body shape. A number of boys presented to our clinic have been particularly concerned about heart disease.

Are boys harder to treat ?

Finally, a brief word about outcome. Opinions tend to vary in the literature about the prognosis of anorexia nervosa in males. Some authors have suggested that 'maleness' is a poor prognostic indicator (eg. Kalucy et al., 1977), whereas others believe that outcome varies according to the presence or absence of certain background and clinical features to a similar extent in both sexes. Hall et al., (1985) found that outcome in the male patients in their study was comparable to female patients at 5 year follow-up. Burns & Crisp (1985) comment upon the "remarkable similarity in outcome pattern" between males and females, but later found that whereas vomiting predicts poor outcome in females, it was associated with good outcome in males (Crisp et al., 1985).

In our own study (Bryant-Waugh et al., 1988) we found that boys and girls differed significantly on two outcome scores. As a group the boys scored less highly on the scale assessing eating behaviour, weight, and weight sensitivity (nutritional status) and also the scale assessing attitudes towards sexual relationships (psychosexual adjustment). However, the number of boys included in this study was very small, and it is not possible at this stage to make any clear statements about potential differences in outcome between boys and girls. Thankfully, some of the boys we have seen at our clinic go on to make complete recoveries (Jonathan was one of them), but other make only partial recoveries or may develop a more chronic form of anorexia nervosa.

REFERENCES

American Psychiatric Association (1980) *Diagnostic and Statistical Manual of Mental Disorders 3rd Edition.* Washington, DC: APA

Bryant-Waugh R., Knibbs J., Fosson A., Kaminski Z. & Lask B. (1988) Long term follow up of patients with early onset anorexia nervosa. *Archives of Disease in Childhood 63: 5-9*

Burns T. & Crisp A.H. (1984) Outcome of anorexia nervosa in males. *British Journal of Psychiatry 145: 319-325*

Burns T. & Crisp A.H. (1985) Factors affecting prognosis in male anorexics. *Journal of Psychiatric Research 19: 323-328*

Crisp A.H. & Burns T. (1983) The Clinical presentation of anorexia nervosa in males. *International Journal of Eating Disorders 2: 5-10*

Crisp A.H., Burns T. & Bhat A.V. (1986) Primary anorexia nervosa in the male and female: A comparison of clinical features and prognosis. *British Journal of Medical Psychology 59: 123-132*

Fichter M.M. & Daser C. (1987) Symptomatology, psychosexual development and gender identity in 42 anorexic males. *Psychological Medicine 17: 409-418*

Fosson A., Knibbs J., Bryant-Waugh R. & Lask B. (1987) Early onset anorexia nervosa. *Archives of Disease in Childhood 62: 114-118*

Hall A., Delahunt J.W. & Ellis P.M. (1985) Anorexia Nervosa in the Male: Clinical features and follow-up of nine patients. *Journal of Psychiatric Research 19 (2/3): 315-321*

Higgs J.F., Goodyear I.M. & Birch J. (1989) Anorexia Nervosa and Food Avoidance Emotional Disorder. *Archives of Disease in Childhood 64: 346-351*

Jacobs B.W. & Isaacs S. (1986) Pre-pubertal anorexia nervosa: A retrospective controlled study. *Journal of Child Psychology and Psychiatry 27: 237-250*

Kalucy R.S., Crisp A.H. & Harding B. (1977) A study of 56 families with anorexia nervosa. *British Journal of Medical Psychology 50: 381- 395*

Slade P. (1982) Towards a functional analysis of anorexia nervosa and bulimia nervosa, *British Journal of Clinical Psychology 21: 167-179*

Sterling J.W. & Segal J.D. (1985) Anorexia nervosa in males: A critical review. *International journal of Eating Disorders 4: 559- 572*

Vandereycken W. & Van de Broucke S. (1984) Anorexia nervosa in males: A comparative study of 107 cases reported in the literature (1970 to 1980). *Acta Psychiatrica Scandinavia 70: 447-454*

CONTRIBUTORS

sine M. Arondeus, Dr.S.
dical Psychologist
ikl. Centrum voor Anorexia and Bulimia Nervosa,
ademisch Ziekenhuis Vrije Free Universiteit,
stbus 7057
07 MB Amsterdam,
derlands.

rin Bell, Dr. Med.
tzin für Innere Medizin, Psychotherapie,
d Psychoanalyse,
ücker Mauspfad 601,
00 Köln 91,
R.D.

chel Bryant-Waugh, B.Sc., M.Sc., D.Phil.,
ncipal Clinical Psychologist,
ot Psychological Medicine
spital for Sick Children,
eat Ormond Street,
ndon WC1
gland

lith Bullerwell-Ravar, Clin. Psychol.
fesseur de Relation et Communication,
.F.A.B., et Université de Paris X
ntre de Psychologie de l'Enfant
Quai d'Orsay,
007 Paris,
nce.

chel Calam, M.Sc., C.Psychol
turer in Child and Adolescent Psychology
ot. Clinical Psychology
versity of Liverpool,
. Box 147
rpool L69 3BX
land

Bridget Dolan, Ph.D., C.Psychol.
Research Fellow & Hon. Therapist
Dept. Mental Health Sciences
St George's Hospital Medical School,
Tooting, London SW17 0RE
England

Inez Gitzinger, Dipl.-Psych.
Psychologin,
Forschungstelle für Psychotherapie,
Christian Belser Str. 79a,
7000 Stuttgart-70,
BRD.

Pat Hartley, Ph.D., C.Psychol, A.F.B.Ps.S.
Lecturer in Psychology
Eating Disorders Project,
Centre for Health Studies,
Salford College of Technology,
Salford M6 6PU.
England.

Werner Köpp, Dr. med.
Uniklinikum Steglitz,
Abt. Psychosomatik,
Hindenburgdamm 30,
1000 Berlin 45
B.R.D.

Malcolm Laing, E.N.
Nurse/Therapist,
The Cullen Centre,
Royal Edinburgh Hospital,
Edinburgh EH10 5HF
Scotland.

Jennifer Munro, B.Sc, C.Psychol,
Research Psychologist,
The Cullen Centre,
Royal Edinburgh Hospital,
Edinburgh EH10 5HF
Scotland.

Maxine Rogers,
Freelance Illustrator,
69a, Castlenau,
Barnes,
London SW13 9RT

Peter Slade, Ph.D., C.Psychol, F.B.Ps.S.
Professor of Clinical Psychology
Dept. Clinical Psychology
University of Liverpool,
Whelan Building, Box 147
Liverpool L69 3BX
England

Rose Stockwell, B.Sc, Dip.C.O.T, B.A.C.acc.
Therapist,
Eating Disorders Clinic
St George's Hospital,
Tooting, London SW17
England

Winny L. Weeda-Mannak, Dr.
Medical Psychologist,
Polikl. Centrum voor Anorexia and Bulimia Nervosa,
Academisch Ziekenhuis Vrije Free Universiteit,
Postbus 7057
1007 MB Amsterdam,
Nederlands.

Ellie van Vreckem,
Klinisch Psychologe Psychotherapeute
U.P.C. Kortenberg,
Leuwensesteenweg 517,
3070 Kortenberg,
Belgium

Walter Vandereycken, M.D., Ph.D.,
Professor of Psychiatry
U.P.C. Kortenberg,
Leuwensesteenweg 517,
3070 Kortenberg,
Belgium